DANCE:
THE STORY OF
KATHERINE DUNHAM

Doubleday Signal Books

BONNIE
PONY OF THE SIOUX
THE JUNGLE SECRET
NORTH POLE: THE STORY OF
  ROBERT PEARY
BASEBALL BONUS KID
CAROL HEISS: OLYMPIC QUEEN
GREEN LIGHT FOR SANDY
SEA TREASURE
THE BLOOD RED BELT
KENDALL OF THE COAST GUARD
RODEO ROUNDUP
NANCY KIMBALL, NURSE'S AIDE
FOOTBALL FURY
CIVIL WAR SAILOR
DINNY AND DREAMDUST
AUSTIN OF THE AIR FORCE
THE LONG REACH
FOOTLIGHTS FOR JEAN
BASEBALL SPARK PLUG
RUNAWAY TEEN
LIGHTNING ON ICE
HOT ROD THUNDER
JUDY NORTH, DRUM MAJORETTE
DIRT TRACK DANGER
ADVENTURE IN ALASKA
CLIMB TO THE TOP
FISHING FLEET BOY
JACK WADE, FIGHTER FOR
  LIBERTY
THE MYSTERY OF HIDDEN
  HARBOR
SCANLON OF THE SUB SERVICE
A SUMMER TO REMEMBER
NAT DUNLAP, JUNIOR "MEDIC"
BLAST-OFF! A TEEN ROCKET
  ADVENTURE
TWO GIRLS IN NEW YORK
THE MYSTERY OF THE FLOODED
  MINE
CATHY AND LISETTE
EVANS OF THE ARMY
HIGH SCHOOL DROP OUT
DOUBLE TROUBLE
PRO FOOTBALL ROOKIE
THE MYSTERY OF BLUE STAR
  LODGE

ADVENTURE IN DEEPMORE CAVE
FAST BALL PITCHER
HI PACKETT, JUMPING CENTER
NURSE IN TRAINING
SHY GIRL: THE STORY OF
  ELEANOR ROOSEVELT
SKI PATROL
BIG BAND
GINNY HARRIS ON STAGE
GRACIE
THREE CHEERS FOR POLLY
SECOND YEAR NURSE
FEAR RIDES HIGH
THE MYSTERY OF THE INSIDE
  ROOM
ARTHUR ASHE: TENNIS CHAMPION
THE MYSTERY OF THE
  THIRD-HAND SHOP
GOING, GOING, GONE
THE KID FROM CUBA: ZOILO
  VERSALLES
GANG GIRL
TV DANCER
ROAR OF ENGINES
DONNA DEVARONA: GOLD MEDAL
  SWIMMER
PETE CASS: SCRAMBLER
BLACK SOLDIER
QUEEN OF ENGLAND: THE STORY
  OF ELIZABETH I
TROUBLE AT MERCY HOSPITAL
TRAPPED IN SPACE
MARTIN LUTHER KING: FIGHTER
  FOR FREEDOM
DANCE! THE STORY OF
  KATHERINE DUNHAM
THE TOMMY DAVIS STORY
FIRST LADY OF INDIA: THE
  STORY OF INDIRA GANDHI
RUNAWAY
SHIRLEY CHISHOLM
THREE WHO SERVED
I WAS A BLACK PANTHER
THE TRUTH ABOUT DRUGS
MIGHTY HARD ROAD

DANCE:
THE STORY OF
KATHERINE DUNHAM

By Ruth Biemiller

Doubleday & Company, Inc.
Garden City, New York

Photos 1, 3 through 10, 17 reproduced from the
personal collection of Katherine Dunham.

LIBRARY OF CONGRESS CATALOG CARD NUMBER 69–11000
COPYRIGHT © 1969 BY DOUBLEDAY & COMPANY, INC.
ALL RIGHTS RESERVED
PRINTED IN THE UNITED STATES OF AMERICA

PREPARED BY RUTLEDGE BOOKS

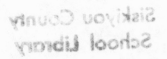

CONTENTS

DANCE:
THE STORY OF
KATHERINE DUNHAM

CHAPTER 1

Indians in the Basement

The little Negro girl gazed in wonder at the Indians dancing about her, waving hatchets, and uttering shrill war cries. Lines of red and yellow and green and white paint on their faces made them look like people from another world. She had never even imagined such things, much less seen them before.

Katherine Dunham was four years old. Her mother was dead. Her father's business kept him traveling. So Katherine and her brother Albert lived in Chicago with their Aunt Lulu. There were lots more Dunham relatives in Chicago, and they were all interested in show business—in acting or dancing or singing.

"I wish I had a pretty feather for my hair," the little

girl thought. "I wish I had paint on my face. I wish I could dance like that!"

"Okay, cut!" yelled Uncle Arthur, who was directing the show. "We will break for five minutes. Then we will try again—and see if we can put some feeling in it!"

Before Katherine's disappointed eyes, the Indians became just people again: cousins and aunts and uncles and friends. But now that the dance was over for the moment, Katherine felt it was safe to leave her seat on the basement stairs.

She pushed her way through the crowd to Aunt Clara, who sat off to one side with a make-up case. Aunt Clara was in charge of costumes, and of making up the dancing people so they looked like Indians.

"Please," Katherine said, tugging at Aunt Clara's skirt, "could I have a feather in my hair?"

Her aunt hesitated a moment. Then she said, "Why not? Would you like some war paint, too? Would you like to be an Indian?"

Katherine could hardly believe it. "Oh, please!"

The little girl sat still as a statue while Aunt Clara carefully drew lines and circles of color on her face—a beautiful scarlet line over each eye, curving sweeps of blue and yellow on her cheeks, a band of white down her nose and along her jaw. Then her aunt chose a big turkey feather and fastened it into Katherine's hair so it stood straight up in back.

"There!" Aunt Clara said. "Now you are as much an Indian as any of the rest of us." And she laughed, as if she had made a joke.

A moment later, Uncle Arthur shouted, "Places, everybody. Take it from the top!"

Katherine had been watching the company practice for days now, so she knew what that meant. "Take it from the top" was show business talk for "Start at the beginning." Well, she was ready.

This time, when the Indians whirled around the basement, practicing their war dance, there was a very little Indian dancing right along with them. Katherine stamped her feet and yelled war cries at the top of her lungs. This was fun—this was the most fun she had ever had!

All of a sudden a pair of arms scooped her up.

"Katherine, baby, you sit over there on the stairs and watch—will you do that?" It was Uncle Arthur, holding her high, away from the others.

Katherine tried to get free. "But I want to dance, too. I know how."

Uncle Arthur grinned at her. "Sure you do." He lowered his voice, as if he didn't want the others to hear. "That's the trouble, baby. You do it so good, you make everybody else look bad. So you just sit over there and watch, will you? That way you don't show them up and hurt their feelings."

Slowly, Katherine went back to her seat on the stairs. She hated just sitting there, watching. She wanted to be in the center of things. And she could dance and sing—hadn't Uncle Arthur just said so? Her feet tapped out the beat and her voice joined the others under her breath. She knew what the trouble was—the same trouble that kept her from doing so many things she wanted to do. She was too little.

"Well, just wait till I get big," she thought. "Then I will do what I want to do. I can dance and sing all the time if I want to—and nobody can stop me!"

The Indian show, called *Minnehaha,* opened in a Chicago theater a short time later. Katherine and her brother Albert were taken to see it.

Sitting there in the audience, watching the performance, made Katherine feel very special. After all, she *knew* those people dancing and singing up there on the stage. Those were her relatives and her friends that everybody in the audience was clapping for.

"That would be a wonderful thing," she told herself. "Not just singing and dancing, but having a whole crowd of people watching you and clapping their hands."

But not everyone liked *Minnehaha*—at least, not well enough. The show closed after a few performances and the company broke up. Aunt Clara left town. Uncle Arthur went back to giving voice lessons in a place called Mecca Flats, on the other side of town. Katherine was left with only Albert and Aunt Lulu, and life was awfully dull.

Aunt Lulu earned a living for them as a hair dresser, and she had to go to work every day. Albert, who was seven, was in school, except once in a while, when there was nobody else for Katherine to stay with. Albert liked school. He hated missing days and then having to do extra work to catch up. Most of the time, Katherine was left with one neighbor or another until Albert came home from school.

"Be a good girl and don't make any trouble," Aunt Lulu would say, when she and Albert left in the morning. Katherine would promise, and most of the time she kept her promise. But oh, the days were so long!

Saturday was better. Albert was home all day, though Aunt Lulu had to work Saturday. But Sunday—! That was the bright spot of the whole week.

All week long, Katherine would ask her aunt every night, "Are we going to Mecca Flats on Sunday?" And because Aunt Lulu enjoyed Sundays at Mecca Flats, too, she always said yes.

Mecca Flats was a big, tumble-down, old apartment building. Uncle Arthur lived there, and so did lots of other people in show business. Record players, turned up high, played a dozen different songs from a dozen different apartments. People sang. People danced. People laughed till the building shook.

Uncle Arthur and his friends were as good as a show, acting out things that had happened to them, or bits from shows they had seen. What fun Sunday was!

Then, one Sunday, something took the edge off Katherine's pleasure. She heard Aunt Lulu tell Uncle Arthur that somebody called Second Cousin was coming to live with them.

"I've got to do it," Aunt Lulu said. "Hard as I work, I can't make ends meet. Second Cousin works nights, so she will be home with Katherine in the day time. That will be a load off my mind. And she will help pay the rent—she works nights as an usher." (Someone who shows people to their seats in a theater.)

Second Cousin moved into Aunt Lulu's flat a few days later.

Katherine didn't like her at first. For one thing, she didn't talk much, and Katherine liked to chatter all day long. For another thing, Second Cousin let the little coal-burning stove that heated the apartment go out as soon as Aunt Lulu left every morning. She would light it again just before it was time for Aunt Lulu to come home.

Katherine hated being cold. But then she found out that Second Cousin was saving money on coal so that she could go to the theater during the day—and take Katherine with her. Second Cousin was like all the rest of the family. She wanted to sing and dance, too. She had the theater bug.

There were two big theaters close by, the Monogram and the Grand, where there were singing and dancing acts, and people telling jokes and acting out short plays. This, Katherine learned, was called vaudeville—and she loved it. Now she was happy again, and the days flew by. Second Cousin went to the theaters hoping by some magic to break into show business. Katherine didn't care what the reason was, as long as she could tag along.

One Sunday, out at Mecca Flats, Katherine heard Uncle Arthur talking about Second Cousin. "That girl's got no talent," he said. "Beats me why she doesn't give up trying after all this time!"

Katherine thought about it. Talent was the difference between being a good singer and a bad one, a good and a bad dancer. Second Cousin didn't have it, so she never got nearer the stage than sitting down in the audience, or being an usher at night. However, as far as Katherine was concerned, Second Cousin was the best baby sitter she had ever had.

By the time she was five, Katherine had seen all the top vaudeville actors. More, she knew all their songs and dances and jokes. Sitting on Second Cousin's lap in the Monogram or the Grand, the words and the music printed themselves on Katherine's mind, never to be forgotten.

Katherine was happy. Week days, vaudeville with Second Cousin. Sundays, Mecca Flats. What more could anyone want from life?

CHAPTER 2

The Russian Princess

"Come here, children. I want to tell you something."
Aunt Lulu, with an open letter on her lap, patted
the sofa on either side of her.

When Katherine and Albert were sitting beside her,
she went on, "I have a letter from your father. Guess
what?"

It couldn't be anything bad, Katherine decided,
judging from the look on Aunt Lulu's face. "He's
coming to see us?" she asked.

"Better than that. Your father is getting married
again. You and your new mother and he are all going
to live in Joliet. Isn't that wonderful?"

Katherine and Albert exchanged glances. Maybe,

Katherine thought, it was wonderful. She had seen so little of her father since her mother died that he was almost a stranger. All she could remembered about him was being held in his lap while he told her stories.

"Is he going to keep on being a traveling salesman?" Albert wanted to know.

Aunt Lulu shook her head. "No. He's going to buy a dry cleaning business. You'll all be together—a family again."

"Except," Katherine added silently, "that his new wife won't really be Mother." No new mother could ever take the place of their own, she thought. How beautiful she had been, with her pale skin and wide dark eyes. Katherine could remember her best sitting at the piano or playing the harp and singing.

But at least, the little girl comforted herself, Father would be at home. They wouldn't be left alone with this new mother.

"Where is Joliet?" Albert asked.

Katherine looked at him. It seemed to her that Albert knew everything. If he didn't know where Joliet was, it must be a far away place.

But Aunt Lulu said, "Oh, just a little way from Chicago. Not far at all. You can come back here sometimes and visit."

Then Katherine knew why Albert had sounded that

way. He didn't want to go. He didn't want to leave his school that he liked so much. Katherine decided she didn't want to go, either. It was fun in Chicago. Sure, they were often cold in winter, and sometimes they didn't have all they wanted to eat. But Aunt Lulu loved them and was good to them. Who could tell what this new mother would turn out to be like?

But she had kind eyes and gentle hands—and, as Katherine soon discovered, a lap just right for sitting on. She made the apartment over the dry cleaning shop in Joliet into a real home for all of them.

She didn't sing and play like their own mother, but she could do so many things! She was a good cook. She kept the house neat and helped Father in the store, too. And she even sewed pretty dresses and ruffled petticoats for Katherine to wear when they all dressed up to go to church on Sundays.

In no time at all, when Katherine heard the word "mother," it was this new mother that came into her mind.

Life was certainly different now from life in Chicago. Joliet was a small town where Katherine and Albert could run and play, instead of a city with dirty streets. There was no vaudeville theater to go to, but there was plenty to make up for that.

Lady Fern, for instance. She was the beautiful

horse Mr. Dunham bought. Week days she pulled the delivery wagon. On Sundays she was hitched to a fringe-topped buggy to take the Dunham family to church and, later, out into the country for long, lazy picnic afternoons.

One of the biggest changes in Katherine's life was that now she went to school with Albert instead of having to stay behind at home. From the start, school was fun. She learned to read, and now she didn't have to depend on Father to tell her stories. In no time at all she could read them for herself in books, instead of just looking at the pictures.

At school the class sang songs—not the same kind that Katherine had heard in the vaudeville theaters or at Mecca Flats, but just as good in their own way. There were games, too, and Katherine discovered that she was good at sports. She learned to play basketball and field hockey, and she entered track events at the school.

After school, there were girls and boys to play with—something Katherine had never known in Chicago, where all her relatives and her relatives' friends were adults. She raced down the hill with them on roller skates when the weather was good, on her sled when the winter brought snow. Sometimes she and her play mates scrambled like mountain goats up the cliff behind the dry cleaning shop on Bluff Street, clinging to vines and rocks, and enjoying the thrill of knowing they might fall at any moment.

Even though she had someone to play with now, Katherine liked to be alone once in a while, to wander around by herself just looking at things and thinking about them and singing little snatches of songs.

One of those by-herself days, Katherine climbed the big hill back of her house and wandered farther at the top than she had ever gone before. She found herself in the back yard of a big brick house. It was closed up, looking as if nobody lived there. But, as Katherine turned away, a little old lady came out the back door.

Katherine thought for a moment she was going to be chased away. Then the little old lady smiled and said hello. "Where do you live?" she asked.

"At the foot of the hill," Katherine replied. Again she turned to go, and again the old lady's voice stopped her. "Why," Katherine thought, "she's lonely."

"My name is Mrs. Jameson," the old lady said. "Would you like to see my house? We could have afternoon tea together."

The house smelled old and dusty inside, and all of the rooms were locked except the living room and the kitchen. Katherine had never seen anything like that living room—it was full of old trunks. One, that looked oldest of all, had brass bands and nail heads decorating its torn leather cover.

Mrs. Jameson fixed a tray with their tea and a plate of cookies. Then she went over to the old leather trunk, opened it and pulled out a scrap book full of pictures of a plump young woman in tights. She was on a stage, Katherine realized with excitement.

"Those are pictures of me, when I was just a girl," Mrs. Jameson told her. "I was with a theater group, and we traveled all over the country. I danced and sang. My, those were the days! One of my dances stopped the show every time. I always had to repeat it."

Till then, Katherine hadn't let herself realize how much she missed going to see vaudeville, or to Mecca Flats where everybody had something to do with show business. It was wonderful to meet someone interested in the same things she was—someone who had actually been up there on stage, listening to the clapping of the audience. Eager questions spilled out, too fast to understand, and she had to repeat them more slowly and clearly.

After that first day, Katherine went back to the big brick house often after school. The old lady's stories and pictures and theater programs were thrilling, but there were even better treasures in the trunk. Fishing around in it, Mrs. Jameson brought out a blue-and-white beaded bag, a green ostrich feather scarf that she called a boa, and a pair of long white kid gloves. She looked at them all closely, turning them over in her hands, then held them out.

"Here, Katherine, these are for you—to remember me by."

"You mean, to keep? For good?" Katherine could hardly believe her luck.

Mrs. Jameson nodded. "For good. Now sit down—yes, you can put them on first—and I will tell you the stories about them and why I've kept them all these years."

Katherine loved the stories and remembered them word for word. At night, she would dig down into her memory and bring up one of the stories she had heard, and then act it out in her head, playing all the parts, before she went to sleep.

Mrs. Jameson's weren't the only stories that fed Katherine's imagination. Mr. Dunham had many to tell, too. After supper, when homework was done, and when he wasn't too tired from a long day in the store, he would tell about the time when he and the children's mother had built a house in an all-white neighborhood.

"I had to stay out there nights with a gun while it

was being built, to make sure nobody broke the windows or burned the place down. But it was worth it. Once we moved in, and the people found out we were nice folks and good neighbors, everything was fine."

Sometimes Mr. Dunham told them about his childhood in Memphis, Tennessee. Other times he told about his own father, and his father's father.

Great-grandfather Dunham had been a slave—not taken from the west coast of Africa, like most, but from Madagascar, the island off the east coast of Africa. Some of his relatives had been Malays, from the islands of south-east Asia. To Katherine, Africa and Asia sounded as far away as the moon. She looked them up on the maps at school.

"Some day," she promised herself, "I will go to those far away places where my ancestors came from. I will go to many places. I will travel all over the world!"

Albert was much more interested in what had happened to his great-grandfather after he had been captured and brought to the United States as a slave. "Tell about Great-grandpa in the Civil War," Albert would urge his father. Those were the stories he liked best.

So Mr. Dunham would tell how his grandfather had saved the lives—and also the silver and other valuables

26

—of the women and children in the Big House. Dodging the fire of the Union Army's guns, he had hitched up a pair of fast horses to the family carriage and had driven them all to safety.

Those stories she heard and remembered helped Katherine in school. Teachers praised the themes she wrote in English class. When she was 11, a national magazine printed a poem she had written. That same year, her story of how the turtle got his shell was published in a magazine for children.

"See what my little girl wrote?" Mr. Dunham would ask, proudly showing the magazine to his customers. And Mrs. Dunham kept copies of the magazine displayed in the living room. Katherine was very proud, although she tried hard to be modest about it.

"Maybe," she thought, "that's what I will do when I grow up—be a writer. I could do both. I could travel and write about what I see when I'm traveling."

Already Katherine somehow knew she wouldn't have any trouble finding something to do when she grew up. The only trouble would be choosing among the many things she would like to do.

One day, when Katherine was 12, the gymnasium teacher stopped her in the hall. "You don't belong to the dance club, do you?" Miss Kirby asked with a friendly smile. "Would you like to take part in the spring dance program anyway? I've noticed how well you move in class."

Katherine forgot her usual shy manner with teachers. "Oh, I'd love to! Really dance—up on a stage? Do you think I could?"

"I'm sure you could," Miss Kirby told her. "At least, come to practice and try."

Katherine's eyes sparkled. "Oh, I will—and thank you, Miss Kirby."

Practices for the dance program were hard work. But they were fun, too. Katherine was only an extra, along with several others, taking the small, short parts as wood creatures and trees and flowers.

When she wasn't dancing, Katherine watched the ones who had the important parts. How good they were—especially one girl, much better than any of the others! She practiced at a bar in the gymnasium, wearing pink satin dancing slippers and dancing way up on the very tips of her toes.

At home, Katherine tried to dance like that, up on the tips of her toes. But she couldn't do it. Perhaps the special shoes had something to do with it.

The night of the spring dance program, Katherine peeked through the dusty velvet curtains and saw her parents and Albert sitting in the audience. She wished she could dance by herself, instead of just being one of the extras. But at least she was up here on the stage, being part of show.

Toward the end of the program, the girl with the pink satin slippers was to do a dance by herself. She wore a costume so beautiful it made Katherine catch her breath—a white fur hat and white kid boots and a red satin jacket. Her skirt was satin, standing out stiffly over starched petticoats. Head high, she leaped out on the stage.

"The Russian princess," Katherine heard someone behind her whisper.

There was strange music, and the Russian princess began to dance. The music grew faster and the girl leaped higher. Finally, she seemed to be sitting on air, arms crossed over her chest, thrusting first one leg forward, then the other.

When she was finished, the audience cheered more than for anyone else. As out of breath as if she herself had been doing the dance, Katherine found the place on the program. A *hopak*—that was what the dance was called.

Now Katherine had a brand new dream—to dance like that girl, to wear a Russian princess costume and whirl and leap around the stage. "I can do it," she told herself. "I can wear that costume and do that dance—and some day I will!"

But she knew she couldn't just do the dance. First she had to learn how.

"Can I take dancing lessons?" Katherine asked her parents the next day. "Miss Kirby says I'd be very good if I had lessons. Please!"

Mr. and Mrs. Dunham exchanged a look, asking each other if they should say yes. Katherine held her breath.

Mrs. Dunham sighed. "Katherine, you know you have to practice piano an hour and half every day after school. And you have homework to do. And you have to do some of the house work, so I can help your father in the shop. Where would you find the time?"

"I will *make* the time," Katherine promised.

She planned her days, somehow fitting in house work and homework, school, piano practice—*and* dancing lessons. Armed with this evidence, she asked her mother and father again. This time they said yes.

Now, three days a week after school, Katherine went to dancing class. With her class mates she circled the gymnasium. She sat and fell and jumped and leaped and stretched—and discovered that there was a bad and a good way to do all these things. The good way felt right when you were doing it, and you weren't so stiff and sore afterward.

But, although she enjoyed every moment, none of

this was the Russian *hopak*. It wasn't toe dancing either, in lovely pink satin slippers.

"Please, could we learn ballet?" Katherine finally got up the courage to ask the teacher.

The teacher laughed. "We don't teach ballet here," she told Katherine. "That comes later. You have to learn to walk before you can run, and it's the same way with dancing. You must learn the simple steps first, before you attempt anything else."

So Katherine went on with the ABC of dance. But the dance of the Russian princess never left her mind. Neither did the pink satin slippers for toe dancing.

"Some day," she told herself. "Some day."

CHAPTER 3

The Blue Moon Café

"Katherine, it's time to go to chapel," Mrs. Dunham called.

Katherine sighed and put down the new *Saturday Evening Post* that had just come in the mail. She had been eagerly awaiting its arrival and the latest chapters in the frightening adventures of Dr. Fu Manchu. Now she had to leave and go to church!

Mrs. Dunham was so active in church work that it sometimes seemed to Katherine that they spent every free moment at the church. Not just services and Sunday school on Sunday, but singing practice and weddings and funerals and basement suppers, and goodness knows what else in between. Always something!

But Katherine answered cheerfully, "Yes, Mother, I'm coming," and hurried to wash her hands and comb her hair. She would enjoy it when she got there, she told herself. She always did.

Members of the church were filing into the chapel as Katherine and Mrs. Dunham reached the small, weather-beaten wooden building. Nods and smiles welcomed them. They went in and sat down.

For a while, Katherine listened to the whispered conversations going on around them. Then she let her thoughts wander and began going over, in her mind, the latest dancing lesson. Turn . . . spin . . . leap . . . come down facing the audience and sink into a graceful bow. . . .

Suddenly Katherine's attention was brought back to the present as she heard a voice say, "If we had a fashion show, the dresses could be sold afterward, and—"

Katherine listened carefully. The members were discussing ways to make money for a new church house for meetings and social events. There was talk of a picnic, a fish fry. Katherine's thoughts rushed off again. She could see herself modeling the latest styles . . . tasting the fish . . . moving among the grown-ups, offering plates heaped high with delicious food.

Suddenly a wonderful idea came into her head.

Maybe . . . would they? Oh, it would be too good to be true, but if they would . . . !

Katherine was so eager to share the excitement of her new idea that she waved her hand in the air for permission to speak. When she received it, she said in a clear, carrying voice, "I would like to organize a cabaret party!"

She felt hot, and then cold. Everyone stared at her. But she hadn't said anything awful! "Please." Now her voice was low, but there was firm purpose in it.

Katherine could hardly listen to the lively discussion that followed. Some of the members were shocked at the very idea of a cabaret in a church. Weren't cabarets wicked, with all kinds of terrible things going on? Others were asking exactly what a cabaret *was*. In this small town, many of the people had never been to one. They were told it was a kind of show, with dancing and singing, and the audience sat at tables to watch it.

While the voices rose and fell, arguing for and against her idea, Katherine's mind raced ahead. She was already planning the music, the dances, the costumes, the food. They had to agree. They *had* to!

Her mother tugged at her sleeve. "Katherine, we are talking to you. Listen!"

They were asking questions, but she could tell that

34

they were not against her idea. Then came their decision. She was to be allowed to run her cabaret!

Already, Katherine could see the evening as a huge success. She would introduce all of the acts. She would be at the piano to accompany the singing, and she would sing a song herself. And she would dance—she would dance the *hopak!*

Katherine's excitement, and her confidence that the evening would be a success, spread to everyone else. Her father arranged to rent the hall used by the Brotherhood of Elks. Even more wonderful, he agreed to perform! In the happy days so long ago when Katherine's real mother had played the harp, Father had played the guitar and had joined her in singing. His favorite song had been "Asleep in the Deep," and now he promised to sing it at the cabaret.

Mrs. Dunham offered to help with the costumes. She was pleased with Katherine's idea, but she was puzzled, too. "Where on earth did you ever get this cabaret idea, Katherine?" she asked. "What a thing for a little girl to think up!"

She was called to wait on a customer before Katherine could reply. Where? In the city, of course! When Father took her to Chicago to visit Aunt Lulu and Uncle Arthur, she would listen to her aunts and uncles and cousins and all their friends talking by the hour. In Chicago, you were just nobody unless you could talk of this show and that vaudeville house. They had made Katherine feel very young and dull, but she was impressed and very interested.

But it wasn't merely the smart talk of theirs that made Katherine want to stage a cabaret of her own. Looking back, she could see how her past had led to this moment. *Minnehaha*, Second Cousin taking her to vaudeville, her friend Mrs. Jameson, and the dance program and lessons—all of these things had been steps toward her cabaret.

And now she would be the star. Mrs. Dunham was already at work on a Russian princess costume.

Katherine also meant to manage, direct, and produce the cabaret. There was room for other acts and for assistants, of course. There was Mrs. McDonald, for instance—a lady with a great past. Years ago, she had toured the country with a theater company, just as Mrs. Jameson had. Now she was a strong member of the church and the wife of a local doctor. She was only too happy to help Katherine with the cabaret.

Together they dug into the trunks which had accompanied Mrs. McDonald on tour. They were filled with tight-waisted dresses in delicious colors, great velvet hats trailing fluffy ostrich plumes, fancy gloves, high-heeled shoes. Katherine was thrilled, but completely at home. After all, this was not her first experience with a person from the stage.

Finally, practices began. Katherine used everything she could remember from the entertainment at the vaudeville theaters, scenes from movies she had seen and thought she had completely forgotten, snatches of songs she had heard in the city streets—they all came back to her now.

There would be a cakewalk, a famous American Negro dance, with Katherine leading the chorus of men and women. Then she would join the girls singing. She would sing her own song, and she would perform a dance. And then, as the final act, Katherine would be the Russian princess of her dreams, dancing the *hopak*.

The night of nights drew near, and everyone was nervous as they tried to get things done in time. At last even the Russian princess costume was finished— but it was not quite what Katherine dreamed of. The skirt was cotton, not satin, and the hat was felt, not fur. Instead of white kid boots, there were white stockings over last summer's white pumps.

But it would have to do and, at any rate, Katherine had no time for feeling disappointed. She was too busy with all the last minute details—the decorations, food, ticket sales, costume changes, getting people on and off the tiny stage. By the time Katherine climbed into bed the night before the show, her mind was spinning.

She woke the next morning with a raging fever.

"Katherine, you stay in bed," her mother said.

"I can't! There's too much to do. I've got to get over to the hall."

"You heard your mother," Mr. Dunham said. "You stay in bed. Getting you well is more important than any show!"

Katherine tossed and turned all morning. "But the final practice!" she pleaded. "I've just got to be there for the last practice!"

"The practice will get along just fine without you," she was told. "Drink this, now."

Katherine burst into tears. She sobbed until her parents gave in and said she could go to the practice —but only on condition she would promise to take it easy.

Katherine jumped out of bed and pulled her clothes on any which way. Grabbing the big box containing her costumes, she raced to the rented hall, which she had called the Blue Moon Café for weeks now, after a song Uncle Arthur used to sing. *Her* Blue Moon Café.

Everybody was milling around. Katherine blew a

whistle. There was a hush as she stepped to the stage to recite the welcome which opened the show.

Katherine opened her mouth. Her lips formed words—but no sound came out. She had lost her voice! She couldn't speak louder than a whisper.

Dr. Williams, the family doctor, came to the hall and looked at her throat. He shook his head. "Those tonsils have to come out," he announced.

Katherine began to cry again. She couldn't help it. After all her plans and work . . . Dr. Williams smiled at her, and from his black satchel he produced some pills.

"You take these, young lady," he told her. "You won't be doing any talking tonight, but maybe you'll be feeling a little bit better. This isn't the end of the world, you know."

It wasn't the end of the world for *him*, Katherine thought bitterly. But for her . . .

"Here, Katherine," said the doctor's wife, a close family friend. "Listen, now, why don't I copy down what you were going to say? Mrs. McDonald could say it just fine, don't you think?"

Katherine's song was crossed off the program. The girls' singing group would be short one girl. Otherwise the show would go on as planned. At least, Katherine's dances were still on the program, and they were Katherine's favorite part.

The next hours were a bad dream. Katherine did everything she could without talking. She helped the food committee and the ticket committee. She sat while Mrs. McDonald put stage make-up on her, and she scarcely recognized herself when Mrs. McDonald finished. Her eyebrows were long and curved, her cheeks and lips and eyelids were all changed by color. Over all there was smooth powder.

Finally, Katherine put on her first costume, pulling the cotton veils close around her. The night was warm, but she was shivering. She peeked through the curtain. The audience was arriving. The people chattered, admiring the decorations. As Katherine watched, she sweated and shivered, and shivered and sweated.

Her mother came over to her. "There isn't a single seat left empty," she said. "Your cabaret is really packed! You'd better begin."

The moment had come. Lights were lowered, and Katherine heard Mrs. McDonald welcoming the crowd. There were some piano numbers, and a chorus sang a song. Then Katherine heard the opening bars of her music. It was time for the maiden from Turkey— time for Katherine Dunham to dance!

She found herself moving gracefully to the center of

the floor. People were clapping. Standing there, she suddenly forgot all she had practiced, all the dance movements she had planned to go with the music. And yet, her body seemed to remember. She moved about, performing the steps, matching the beat of the music, and ending right when the music did. Then she disappeared through the curtain, not hearing the cheers. As long as she lived, she would never be quite sure what happened after that. She supposed that she changed her costume, that she took part in the rest of the dances.

She couldn't help but remember the *hopak*—the whirling girl in the red-and-white costume of the Russian princess was the hit of the evening! There was loud clapping, and shouts of "More! More!" Katherine repeated her dance, coming back out to leap and whirl again, taking strength from her cheering audience.

That night, in true cabaret style, the dancing lasted late. But the Blue Moon Café's leader, director, and star—the Russian princess—went home to bed.

Katherine felt much better the next day, as soon as she was told that her party had cleared 76 dollars. The hall held 400 people, and tickets cost only 25 cents each, so the Blue Moon Café had been a complete success.

CHAPTER 4

Troubled Times

Starting high school is a big moment for any teen-aged girl. Katherine looked forward to it, yet she felt nervous when the day finally arrived.

"I hope I can do as well as you have, Al," she said to her brother as they walked to school together. Albert was a class leader, good in his studies, in sports and in music.

He grinned down at her. "Sure you will! You always have been good in your studies and in sports, haven't you? And wait till you get into the school library. We will never see you without your nose in some book!"

Katherine laughed. It was true, she did love to read. And she had been looking forward to the library.

From the books that Albert brought home, she knew the school had some that the public library lacked. She hoped there'd be some good ones about Africa and Asia, not to mention the Caribbean Islands. The more she read about those islands, the more her interest grew. It would be wonderful to visit them sometime. But in the meantime, reading about their strange sights and customs was nearly as good.

It was more than the school library that had made Katherine look forward to starting high school. There would be parties and dances, maybe even going out with boys! Her parents, especially her father, were awfully strict about the company she kept. They had said many times that she was too young to date. Still . . .

Katherine studied hard and did get better marks than most of her class mates. She worked just as hard at sports, going out for basketball and the girls' track team. She practiced until she became a regular winner in other events. She was easily elected president of the Girls' Athletic Association. But no matter how busy she was, she still found time to practice her dancing.

Katherine handled school well, but life at home was harder to manage. Her father no longer played the guitar or told stories. There were no more rides into the country for family picnics on Sunday afternoons, either. Mr. Dunham's mood had changed completely. Now whippings were common. His leather strap left marks on Katherine's and Albert's arms and legs and backs. Many nights, Katherine lay awake, trying not to hear the violent quarrels taking place in her parents' bedroom.

The change in Mr. Dunham was caused by many things. He was unhappy and worked too hard. Katherine blamed the dry cleaning business for making her father an enemy, and she and Albert grew to hate it. Mr. Dunham drove himself hard to keep up with the steady growth of his business. He also wanted his wife and his son and daughter to spend every possible minute in the shop. The work never ended—mending, sewing labels, pressing, keeping accounts, making deliveries, lifting rugs into the huge carpet cleaning machine. The sounds of machinery and the hiss of steam irons drowned out all talk in the dirty work rooms. The air was always full of dust and fumes. The shop smelled of burned cotton. It was not a healthy place for growing children.

Dancing lessons, music lessons, athletics, even homework kept Albert and Katherine out of the shop much of the time. Mr. Dunham felt that anything the two teen-agers did on their own threatened his business. He hated to see Albert studying his books because the books reminded him that his son was determined to go on to college instead of becoming a partner in the cleaning business.

But worse than the books were Albert's music lessons. They took time, and they also cost money. Albert's love for music came from both his father and his own mother. But this made no difference to Mr. Dunham. The lessons caused many bitter family arguments, and Mrs. Dunham argued on Albert's side, not on her husband's.

"We are staying home too much," Mrs. Dunham declared one day. "We are all getting on each other's nerves this way. We need to get away from the house and the shop. Why, we never go on picnics any more, or visit in the city like we used to."

"No time," her husband grunted. "Money doesn't grow on trees—you have to work for it. And we could all work a sight harder than we have been."

"We could all work ourselves right into our graves," Mrs. Dunham answered. "And we are not going to do that. My friend down in Alton has been after me to come visit her and bring Katherine, and we are going to do just that. Then after we get back, you and Albert can go visit the Chicago relatives, and Katherine and I will run things while you are gone."

Katherine and Albert exchanged looks. They could imagine about how much chance there was of their father agreeing to such a plan.

But Katherine and her mother did go to Alton. Mrs. Dunham simply packed up and went off with Katherine without asking permission.

The train trip was long, and seemed far more interesting than the short run up to Chicago. There was the fun of seeing friends again, and talking on and on as they caught up on one another's activities since their last get-together. Mrs. Dunham spoke proudly of the cleaning business and her husband's ambition. With the distance between, it was almost possible to forget the bitter quarrels and long, tiring hours of work.

"Tonight we will go over to St. Louis, down Chouteau Street," Mrs. Dunham's friend planned. "They're having quite a time, as good as the New Orleans Mardi Gras!"

Katherine's eyes lit up. She had read about the Mardi Gras, with costumes and parties. New Orleans was so far away, she didn't dare hope to go there. But St. Louis was just across the river from Alton.

Chouteau Street was wonderful. Crowds of people jammed the sidewalks and even the street. They were living it up, laughing, hugging, calling out to each other. They wore crazy costumes and leaped wildly about. They broke into snatches of song and dance. Even lined up to buy fish, they weren't merely people waiting in line: they were singing and all doing a little dance. Music came out of every doorway, making Katherine's spine tingle with pleasure. She had heard the blues on records at Mecca Flats, but these were the *live* blues, straight from the soul.

"Why, it's as good as a stage or a movie!" Mrs. Dunham declared. "Not quite real, at all!"

Katherine smiled. It was *better* than any show, for she was in the middle of it, not watching from the audience. But the crowds did look special, like people on stage. Katherine suspected that she and her mother and their friend were the ones who looked odd to the others, being so properly dressed and behaving so carefully. She wondered why it seemed necessary always to act just so, like the rich white people in the movies, instead of just being themselves, enjoying the life they were living.

Going back to Joliet and the tiring work in the shop was a let down after the excitement of the trip. But at least memories of the visit gave Katherine something thrilling to think about as she did her chores.

Then Albert received important news. He had been

given a scholarship! His way would be paid through the university.

"I will be leaving home at the end of this term, then," he said. "Go on up to Chicago, and—"

"You'll do no such thing!" Mr. Dunham shouted, and slapped Albert hard. "You are staying right here, where you belong, helping me!"

Albert ran from the house, his father chasing and hitting him and then, when Albert got ahead of his father, threatening him.

All that afternoon and evening, Mrs. Dunham followed her husband about, pleading for the boy. But both she and Katherine could tell there would be more quarreling and violence.

When Albert came back home, it was so late that Katherine and her parents had gone to bed. Katherine heard her brother settle down in the dining room, as usual, to do his homework. But he had hardly had time to open his books before Mr. Dunham came charging down the stairs and turned off the lights.

The next afternoon, Katherine returned from school to find her mother gone. She thought at first that Mother was just out on an errand or visiting. But the breakfast dishes were still in the sink, unwashed. A quick check of her parents' room showed that the suitcase and most of Mrs. Dunham's clothes were gone, too.

Katherine looked at the dirty breakfast dishes. "I'd better get to work," she told herself, turning on the water. "Looks like nobody else is going to do them."

In a way, the fact that Mrs. Dunham had disappeared was no surprise. Katherine found she had somehow known that her mother could not go on forever this way, working too hard and unable to stop the whippings and the mean words Mr. Dunham yelled at the entire family. Life at home had been getting worse with each passing day.

"Did she leave you a note?" Albert was standing in the doorway.

Katherine shook her head. "Did she leave you one?"

"No." Albert picked up the towel and began to dry the dishes. "She will come back," he said. "She has to."

"Will you go to the city if she doesn't?"

"I *have* to. But surely she will be back before then."

Katherine started to cry. She tried hard to stop, but she couldn't. She wanted to be brave and have her brother admire her. She admired him so much. But home was going to be horrible without Mother standing between them and Father. Mother always tried to make them see what was driving Father and causing

49

his bad humor. She reasoned with him so he would be more understanding.

"Katherine—"

"What?" Katherine sobbed. She blew her nose hard and tried to blink back the hot tears.

"Wouldn't you like to go to Chicago, to the university, too? After you finish high school, I mean?"

Katherine managed a small smile. It was a nice idea, and nice of Albert to try to help her this way. But she didn't dare think of the city and the university. She would have to help Father in the shop, and that would be the end of everything. She was trapped.

"I'd never get a scholarship, the way you did," she said.

"Never mind that. By the time you are ready, I will be able to help you. I will be out and have a good job then. And you can work while you are studying. It couldn't be any harder than you've got it now. Then, after you have finished at the university, you can do anything. Why, you could even go to Africa!"

Katherine shook her head at him, smiling. That Albert! Many times before, they had shared forbidden adventure magazines, reading about Africa and dreaming of going there some day. She wiped away her tears, feeling better. Nothing was quite so bad when

Albert was there, smiling at her. He always found something for her to look forward to, to dream about.

"You've got to have the dream first," Albert said, his thoughts following hers. "If you are willing to work for it, you can make any dream come true!"

CHAPTER 5

How Will It End?

"Albert! Mother's home!" Katherine had hardly been able to wait to tell him.

Albert, tired lines showing on his face from the delivery rounds, lit up. "No fooling? Back to stay? Uh—Father?"

"Tickled pink," Katherine assured him.

The days without Mrs. Dunham had been bad ones. She had written to each of them, letting them know she was with her brother in Wisconsin, caring for his sick wife. She would return when she could, she had promised—provided Mr. Dunham thought things over and would change his ways and treat them all better.

Her absence had been hard on all of them. Mr.

Dunham had been completely upset by her loss, not sure she would return. His business had started going to pieces, even though he worked Katherine and Albert extra hard and hired someone to take Mrs. Dunham's place in the shop. Without her help and ability to smooth things over, nothing went right. The business didn't even pay. Katherine knew he'd written asking Mother to come home and promising improvement, but she had shared his feeling that Mother might not really come.

And now she was back, and cooking them an extra special supper!

She came flying out to give Albert a hug and kiss, exclaim at how tired and thin he was, and to chase him in to get cleaned up to eat, all in one breath. He obeyed, grinning. Mother was back and Father was laughing and joking almost the way he used to do. Everything was going to be all right!

But peace at home didn't last long. No matter how they all tried, quarrels were frequent. Finally, Albert and his father really fought, hitting at one another until a man working in the shop dashed up the stairs and hauled them apart.

Mr. Dunham glared at Albert, breathing hard. "Get

out of this house! And don't ever let me catch you in it again!" he thundered.

Albert gave him a long, level look, then he turned on his heel. Within minutes he was gone, taking with him only some books.

Katherine was desperate. Albert was gone. Mother had left once, and every time Katherine came home she was afraid she would find Mother was gone again. What would happen if she were left alone with her raging father? She couldn't stand it!

Finally, the time Katherine dreaded came. With quiet dignity, Mrs. Dunham announced that she had rented a house, and was leaving.

"Katherine, you are coming with me," she said, turning to the girl. "You go in and pack your clothes."

In their new tiny house, Mrs. Dunham and Katherine talked and talked. Mrs. Dunham would sew for other people to pay the bills. "You stay in school and graduate. That's more important than getting a job right away."

"Well—" Katherine said slowly. She felt that she ought to be doing something to help. "Well, maybe so. I will be able to get a better paying job after I graduate. And I can work after school and on Saturdays till then."

Mr. Dunham joined in some of the family conferences after a while. He came to the house to ask Mrs. Dunham whether she would sew for him. She considered. It might be best for all of them for the break to be complete, not see anything at all of one another. Yet . . . she needed the money as much as he needed her help. It seemed silly to turn down his request.

"And I will give you some money, besides, to help support Katherine," he offered. "She can come work in the shop after school. That's fair, isn't it?"

Even though Katherine didn't like working in the shop any better than she ever had, life was so much better! She enjoyed living with Mother and the way they could laugh and talk together without fear. She liked getting acquainted with the new family in town without having to listen to her father tell her she was wasting her time.

The new family's son, Bill, was Katherine's age and he was in some of her classes. He was tall and athletic and had a great sense of humor.

One afternoon, Katherine was standing on the school steps when she heard someone ask, "Walk you home?"

Katherine could hardly believe her ears. She knew, without turning her head, that it was Bill. For a moment she thought she was dreaming—she had day dreamed about this often enough! But it was true.

Then she remembered her father. "I guess Bill hasn't heard yet," she thought bitterly. "Nobody's told him Father doesn't allow me to date."

But it was broad daylight, and walking together wasn't dating. Besides, their families went to the same church and were friendly, so how could Father object?

"Why not?" she said, smiling up at him with the spark which made her seem even prettier than she was. "Only, I'm not going home. I have to go to the shop and help Father till supper time."

Bill smiled. "So what? It's all the same direction."

They walked together, laughing and talking, as far as the bridge down the street from the shop. It was so much fun, being with someone nice! There wasn't much to say, at first, but conversation became easier as they got acquainted and discovered interests in common.

Before long, the walk became an after-school habit.

"Wear my letter?" Bill asked one afternoon as they lingered at the bridge, not wanting to go their separate ways.

Again Katherine could hardly believe what she was hearing. Her eyes shone. All the lucky girls who dated were sewing the gold wool letters that the boys had won in sports on to their navy-blue sweaters—and all of the other girls were envying them. Now Bill was giving her his letter.

After supper, she very carefully sewed the letter onto her sweater. Mrs. Dunham assumed Katherine had won the letter herself, and was pleased, and Katherine didn't explain. Mother might feel bound to remind her of Father's ban on dating.

Mr. Dunham was quick to guess the truth, for he had already seen her walking with Bill, or lingering at the bridge with him. Several times he had stopped and ordered her into the delivery truck, just as if she were a small child, driving her the rest of the way to the shop.

When he saw the letter, he blew up. "Don't you let me catch you wearing that again! You know what I've told you! You give it right back!"

"But why?" Katherine pleaded. "Father, we are not dating. We are just friends and walk together."

"Don't you argue with me! You do as I say. You hear me?" His voice rose in a threatening roar.

Mr. Dunham watched Katherine more and more. He allowed her only one Saturday afternoon a month for social activities. Katherine tried going to football games, but after a while she stopped. The other girls had boys to go with, or went in a group. It was no fun to go alone.

The same thing was true for basketball games, and skating, and track meets. Katherine began to spend her free Saturday afternoons in the library, reading. Library work would be pleasant, she thought. Dancing was wonderful, but she had been warned often enough of the difficulty of achieving a successful career in show business. She supposed she ought to train for something practical, too, as a means of making a living. She loved to read, and she loved the very smell and feel of books, so why not library work?

Life sometimes changed, but it didn't seem to improve. Katherine's parents continued to quarrel, even though they lived apart. Often it was about money for Katherine's clothing or school books, or food money for Albert.

Albert's health was poor from living in rooms without heat, going without food and sleep, and working at night so he could study in the day time. It was a constant worry to Katherine, not knowing whether he was sick or well. If only he were closer, so she could see him! If by some wild miracle, she could get to attend the university in Chicago, she would be able to keep an eye on him.

If only she could go to Chicago! Just get away from the constant fighting between her parents.

Besides, she realized this town had nothing more to offer her. Even her dancing was at a stop. Her teachers said she should go on to the fine dancing teachers in the city, but how could she? At any rate, when could she practice? A few moments stolen here and there were nothing, especially with Father saying that if she had time to prance around, she had more time to help in the shop.

What she needed—if her teachers *were* right about her talent—was long hours of practice, many hours every day, if she would ever develop her talent and accomplish anything in the dance. And maybe, as people kept telling her, only a few who wanted to be dancers ever succeeded in reaching the top.

Katherine had a deep feeling that she could be one of those to succeed. It wasn't just wanting to show off, either, as her father accused her. True, a cheering audience would be wonderful. But the important thing was dancing itself, the good, strong feel of having her body under control and moving so gracefully. She had to find some way to keep on dancing!

Then, suddenly, a wonderful thing happened. Katherine was invited by one of her father's relatives to a party in the city.

"We just won't tell your father what you are going to do—you know how he is," Mrs. Dunham said firmly. "We can tell him you are going to go visit his relatives, and that's enough for him to know. No need to get him all upset! Now, I will fix up a big basket of good food, and you take that to Albert. You know he isn't eating right, up there by himself."

Next thing she knew, Katherine was settling herself into a seat on the train, the big picnic basket at her feet. She felt so alive and free!

"Being alone is not being lonely," Katherine thought with surprise. "Right here and now, all by myself, life is beautiful!"

She wasn't wild about what was waiting for her in Chicago—a gay party where everybody knew everybody else and she would feel left out. Besides, although she loved to dance and was a good dancer, she didn't often have a partner. Katherine was tall, and few of the boys her age had caught up to her in height.

Another thing, the party clothes her mother made would never seem quite right beside the dresses other girls bought in Chicago's smart shops. And Katherine was not used to being with boys. She was not at ease with them. She had trouble talking to them and didn't have a "line," like the other girls.

All the same, going to Chicago meant getting away

from the troubles at home, and that was wonderful. Besides, there would be good music at the party. If no one asked her to dance, she could sit with Aunt Clara or Aunt Lulu or one of the other older relatives and listen to the music. . . .

The train finally bumped and hissed to a stop. The LaSalle Street Station was filled. People hurried in all directions, and the large, marble station gleamed with electric lights.

And then she saw Albert waving to her. He had come to meet her train! Katherine wanted to run and throw her arms around him and tell him how glad she was to see him. But she was afraid he might not like that. And anyhow, she was carrying her suitcase and the heavy basket of food.

So she just walked up to him, hiding her feelings, and said, "Hi!"

"Hi! All set for the round of parties?" Albert eyed her bag and basket. "Don't tell me you need all that room for your clothes! Where's this party going to be, anyhow?"

"The dance hall," Katherine told him. "Mother sent all kinds of good things for you. A whole apple pie, even. It would have served you right if I'd eaten it on the way!"

Albert laughed. "The South Side Dance Hall? It's

enormous. The college clubs use it for all their big parties." He sounded a little sad. Albert was a senior now at the university. His job and studies left him little time for having fun. "Who's playing, the Earl or the Duke?"

"Earl Hines, I think. Ellington's gone back to New York." She looked at her brother, then got up enough courage to beg, "Come on and go with me."

Albert gave her a look that said there wasn't a chance.

"Oh, Albert, please! It will be awful being extra. Please?"

"Well, just for the first hour," Albert agreed.

"You are learning to handle yourself, Katherine," he went on. "You'll do fine, once you get away from home. You haven't forgotten about coming up here to the university, have you?"

Katherine shook her head. "Forgotten about it? I thought of it all the way up here! But I still don't see how I could."

"We will find some way. When you really want to do something, a way opens up if you are willing to work hard for it and keep your eyes open."

The firm note in Albert's voice convinced her. She would find a way. She would get to the university, or at least manage to come up here to live and work and take the kind of dancing lessons she needed. And then the world would open for her—Africa, Asia, all the places she dreamed about.

That spring, Albert sent Katherine an application form for a civil service examination. The examination might get her a job as a junior library assistant in the Chicago public library system.

"Katherine, that sounds just right for you, the way you love books," her mother said. "You get right on with filling that out and sending it in."

Katherine frowned over the application. "Yes, but, Mother, I'm not quite old enough—see the age one must be? And I ought to be living in Chicago to get it, oughtn't I? And, look here—if I get the job, I'd have to start work two weeks before graduation!"

Mrs. Dunham took the application and studied it. "Just little things," she stated. "You give them your cousin Fanny June's address—you'd be staying with her anyway till you find a room of your own. And you will be the right age by the time you go to work. About graduation—well, if you get the job, we will find some way. I will go talk to the principal about it. And you may not even get the job, so no sense getting in a state about it. Just go ahead and send it on in."

Laughing, Katherine obeyed. If Mother thought it

was all right, then it was. And perhaps this was the way opening up which Albert had talked about. She mailed the letter with a little prayer, and waited.

Finally the answer arrived. She was accepted!

Now to solve the problem of graduation.

"Oh, what a day!" Katherine sighed with pleasure. "This dream job! And Mother, Bill wants me to go to the basketball game with him—you know, the one to decide who will be state champions. I'd love to, but I told him Father would never let me. Bill just won't take no for an answer, though. He finally said he was going to go ask Father's permission. I hope Father doesn't hit the ceiling, but I bet he will."

Mrs. Dunham rolled her eyes and nodded. Knowing Mr. Dunham, it seemed all too likely that he would never approve. Well, at least, now that they weren't all living in the same house, the worst of his fury should be over before they saw him.

They had just finished doing the supper dishes when the front door burst open and Mr. Dunham raged in. His face twisted with anger. He accused Katherine of horrible things.

Katherine stared at him, not believing as she heard the awful words he screamed at her. Then a quiet strength filled her, and she heard herself answering back as she had never dared to before.

When her father slapped her face hard, she told him, "That's the last time, Father—the last time. You are never going to touch me again!"

She turned to the closet. She got her suitcase from the shelf. This solved the job-graduation problem. She wouldn't try to find a way to graduate. She would go straight up to Chicago.

Not realizing that everything between father and daughter had now changed for good, Mrs. Dunham was pleading, as though nothing much had happened, "Katherine, tell your father you didn't mean it! Don't leave this way! You should not have struck her—she's a young lady now! Katherine, don't you go away mad like this!"

CHAPTER 6

This Is Being Alive!

Katherine looked around the room, wondering where to begin. It seemed strange, almost scary, to think that now she was on her own, living in Chicago. There was so much to do to get settled . . . and yet she was strangely unwilling to start.

"I guess I'm afraid," she said to her brother Albert, who was helping her move in.

"Afraid of what?"

Katherine shook her head. "Oh, I don't know. Afraid to get everything put away here because when I'm settled, then what will I do? I'll have so much time on my hands!"

"No, you won't. Just wait and see. Pretty soon

you'll be so busy you won't be able to find time for everything. You want to take dancing lessons again, don't you?"

"You know I do! Yes, I'll have to find a school, and then the lessons will take up a lot of my time, I guess."

"And you have your job at the library," Albert reminded her. "That will take up most of your time during the day."

"I know. But that's only for this summer."

"In the fall, you'll be going to the university. And you'll have to find another job, too. You have to earn your living. Believe me, you will be so busy you won't know where to turn." He bent over and opened a box of books. "Where do you want these?"

Katherine pointed to a shelf in the corner. "Over there, I guess." She sighed. "This will seem like home to me before long, won't it?"

Albert grinned at her. "Of course it will. Think how much better it is going to be. You are your own boss, now. There is nobody to yell at you and hit you. You have a place to live. You have a job. Why, Katherine, you are on top of the world!"

His good mood was catching. She smiled back at him. "It's just that—oh, everything is strange. But I bet that by a week from now, I will feel as if I'd lived here forever."

Albert nodded. "If you are not too busy to notice! You are going to love your job, I'm sure of that. Pretty good, isn't it, you being assigned to the best branch library in the whole city?"

"I just hope I can do the work." But she was feeling better. She had a lot to look forward to—the library job, a new dancing school, the university in the fall. True, she was tired. She missed Mother and Bill— even Father—but there was no reason to be so gloomy.

The branch library turned out to be in a beautiful, park-like section of the city. The only Negroes here, Katherine realized, worked as servants.

The young woman at the front desk stared when Katherine introduced herself. "You are *who?* Oh—of course! I expected a—well, an older person, I guess." She looked down at the desk top for what seemed like a very long time. Finally she said, "I think you'd better see the head of the library." She pointed. "That door over there."

The head of the library was in her private office, a small and proper woman behind a large desk. Magazines, books, and papers were arranged in neat piles. She stood up, surprised, when Katherine appeared in the doorway.

"I'm the new girl, Katherine Dunham."

The head of the library sat down again. She, too, studied the top of her desk. "Katherine Dunham," she said at last. "The new girl? Well—we had better get to work, hadn't we? One of the assistants will—will show you where your locker is and—well, tell you how we do things here. We have always had reason to be proud of this library. You must have done extremely well on the examination. We get only the cream of the crop."

With as few words as possible, one of the assistants showed Katherine around.

Books were old friends to Katherine. She felt at home among them. The ink pads and date stamps and card files were no problem. Library work seemed simple enough, she told herself.

Katherine wasn't surprised that the other workers stared at her curiously. But the people who came to use the library stared, too. Probably, she decided by the middle of the morning, the fact that she was colored bothered them. Well, she felt a little strange, herself, not seeing even one other Negro. "But I will soon get used to that," she thought, "and they will get used to me, too."

A staff meeting was called late in the morning, and Katherine was left in charge of the front desk. Right after the meeting, a new lunch schedule was posted on the bulletin board. There had been two lunch periods before. Now there were three. Katherine had the third period all to herself.

After lunch, Katherine was given her permanent job. She was sent to the book room—where the public could not see her—and set to cataloging books. The other assistants paid no attention to her.

"It's not so bad," she told Albert that night. "They aren't friendly, but they aren't nasty, either. It's just that I've never encountered anything like it before.

"I've been lucky, I guess. Anyway, I'm not going to let it bother me. I've lived through worse. It's better than working in the cleaning shop. Besides, I didn't get the job to make friends—I got it to support myself."

Katherine kept that thought firmly in mind. The really important thing would happen in the fall. She would be going to the university. The big problem now was to decide what to study when she got there. Already, Albert had brought her a catalog of the courses offered, and had begun to introduce her to people who might be helpful in making the right choice.

It turned out to be a wonderful summer. Katherine had a job with books. She felt at home with them even if she didn't with the other people who worked in the library. She had a place of her own to live in, could make her own decisions. And she had a college catalog to dream over. She felt as if a great door to the world had finally opened, and she was standing with one foot on the door step, ready to walk in.

It was the grown-up world that was waiting for her, she knew. She had left her childhood world behind her. There would be new friends for her, she was certain. As Albert's sister, she was already receiving friendly attention from people who knew him. Yes, there would be plenty of helping hands.

"But of course," she told herself, "the main part of it will be up to me. That's why it's so important to be absolutely sure that I choose the right courses. Only— I don't know what the right courses are. I just can't make up my mind what I want to be!"

At least, she thought, she didn't have to worry about doing well in college. Although she admitted that Albert had "the real brains in the family," she was not by any means a poor student. She had done well in Latin and French, and had really enjoyed her English literature courses, doing all the required reading and more.

"But it's more than just loving to read," she told Albert. "It's the exploring, the finding out. I really want to know what makes people behave as they do. For instance, I'd love to know why the others at the library treat me so coldly. Do they really think I'm not as good as they are? Did their parents tell them scare stories about Negroes when they were children? Why do they act that way? That's what I'd really like to study at the university—courses that tell you what makes people tick."

She held up the college catalog. "Why people behave the way they do—that's what I want to take, but it's not in here. Or if it is, I just don't recognize it by the name they call it."

"You have always been interested in that kind of thing, haven't you?" Albert asked thoughtfully. "I remember how you used to sit and listen to Aunt Lulu's stories about life out in the back woods, and the Indian relatives, and all. And Father's stories about the Civil War. And there was the old lady in Joliet who used to be on the stage. Yes—I understand what you mean."

Katherine nodded. "What really did it for me was the trip Mother and I took to visit her friends in Alton, and seeing those people in St. Louis. They were larger than life, somehow. I've wondered about them ever since."

Restless, she walked to the window, looked out, turned back to the room again. "Somehow," she said suddenly, "all that—the stories, the people in St. Louis—seems more real to me than what happens

Katherine Dunham and her brother Albert as children.

Katherine Dunham with her husband John Pratt, who has designed many of the dresses and sets for her dances.
UNITED PRESS INTERNATIONAL

Katherine is made an honorary citizen of Haiti and a Commander of the Legion of Honor of Haiti, 1961.

Katherine Dunham with Vanoye Aikens, one of the best-known dancers in her company.

Katherine Dunham is shown with a collection of African drums belonging to the museum at Alton, Illinois.

Katherine Dunham has an audience with President Leopold Senghor and Minister S. Diop during her visit to Senegal in 1962. Besides being the leader of his country, President Senghor is famous as a poet and writer.

Katherine Dunham with friends at the School of Arts, Dakar, Senegal, 1965.

Katherine with the guardian of the Dynamique Museum in Dakar, Senegal.

Katherine with two students of the School of Fine Arts in Gorée, Senegal.

(Above) Katherine with the Royal Moroccan troupe. (Bottom left) Katherine presents Haitian paintings to the Government of Morocco. Here she is shown with King Hassan of Morocco's uncle. (Bottom right) In her world-wide travels Katherine Dunham has collected many magnificent jewels. Here she is shown with some of her treasures.

On a warm afternoon a steamer docks in a Caribbean port. A Woman with a Cigar brings her baggage ashore. This is one of Katherine Dunham's most famous dances.
PHOTO FRED FEHL

In Bahiana, Katherine is a woman from Bahia. As fine Brazilian rope weavers work away, she gets caught in their rope. And winding her way into their midst, she sings a song. PHOTO FRED FEHL

PICTORIAL PARADE

UNITED PRESS INTERNATIONAL

PHOTO FRED FEHL

L'Ag'ya is a tale of magic from the island of Martinique. Katherine Dunham dances the role of a young girl, Loulouse. She loves Alcide, but is also loved by the wicked Julot who seeks the help of the King of the Zombies (who has the power to bring the dead back to life) in order to win her. With his help Julot gets a strong love charm, and Loulouse begins to dance for him. Alcide breaks free from the magic power. They fight, Julot kills him, and Loulouse is left alone with the body of her lover.

Katherine, arriving at Kennedy Airport, New York, gives an unscheduled dance.
UNITED PRESS INTERNATIONAL

Katherine with a young friend beside the sea.

Katherine Dunham's dancers rehearse on the beach near Copenhagen, Denmark. They all attend the Dunham School, where they are trained in the Dunham technique.

NORDISK PRESSEFOTO FROM PICTORIAL PARADE

every day. Even now, when I'm here and I'm free, and out of all that trouble at home."

She stopped, picked up the catalog and held it out. "The point is, I don't want to get bogged down in a bunch of stuff that doesn't mean anything to me, that isn't really alive. Am I crazy? What do you think?"

Albert grinned, spreading his hands. "Well, you are crazy, all right. You always were. Aside from that, yes, I can see that you are not going to settle down and be an English major and then go teach school till you marry some nice young doctor or lawyer. Not my little sister!"

"Well, then, what *am* I going to do?" she demanded. "It will be silly to study unless I'm aiming at some goal. I might take all the wrong courses before I ever found the right one."

"You might try anthropology," Albert said, almost as if talking to himself. He reached for the catalog, turned its pages. "Yes, here it is. Anthropology—the science of man."

"What's it all about?" Katherine asked. Science had been her worst subject in school.

"It's a fairly new field," Albert told her, "especially the way it is taught in this country. I think you'd like it, because it sounds just like what you were describing."

"But what would I study?" Katherine wanted to know.

"There are lots of fields in anthropology. But knowing you, I bet you'd end up studying the history and development of cultures. Why, you might even end up over in Africa, studying folklore—you know, the beliefs and customs of a people."

"Folklore? I think I'd like that." Katherine thought about it, and the more she thought, the better the idea sounded. "Why," she said, finally, "I could even dance it. I mean, I'd learn a lot I could use in making up new dances. And the dances of a country are a part of its folklore. Oh, I'd like anthropology!"

Albert laughed. "I wondered how long it would be before you mentioned the word *dance*," he teased. "I was beginning to think you'd lost all interest in dancing."

Katherine shook her head. "You know better than that. I just was waiting to find the right major, so I could work dancing into it!"

Katherine felt she ought to pinch herself to make sure she wasn't dreaming. By the time she started at the university in the fall, dancing was more a part of her life than she had ever dared hope it could be. She kept up with her lessons at dancing school, she took dance classes at the university and—just as she had predicted—study of the dance was a part of her work in anthropology. The dance, she found, played an important part in the origins and customs of mankind.

"I wish my library job had been permanent, not just for the summer," she wrote to her mother. "I've got to find another job now, and chances are it won't be as pleasant as working in the library. Worse yet, I might have to work longer hours to make enough money, and that would mean less time for dancing. I spend every possible minute dancing now—and how I love it! I'm meeting lots of nice people in classes, too, and making friends."

One of those new friends gave Katherine an idea. The girl, who had been watching Katherine in one of the dance classes, said to her later, "You ought to be a teacher. You are so much better than the rest of us in class, you ought to be teaching dancing!"

Katherine talked it over with Albert that night. "Do you suppose I could?" she asked. "That would be just about perfect—to make money from the thing I like to do best! I do know enough about dancing to teach, I think."

Albert nodded slowly. "It's a wonderful idea. You'll be dancing and earning your living, both at the same time. And I believe," he said, thinking out loud, "the way to do it is to rent a loft where you can live and also hold your dancing classes. Katherine, I think it is going to work. You can do it if anybody can!"

With Albert's help, a suitable loft was found. The new friends Katherine made, as well as Albert's friends, helped by sending her students. Sooner than she had believed possible, Katherine was in business.

The dancing classes and the recitals—stage programs—that Katherine and her students gave brought in enough money to keep her going. But working with students in a group was important for another reason. It gave Katherine a chance to work on choreography—planning how a complete dance would look, choosing which steps to include, and when and how to use them.

Some teachers, Katherine had discovered, planned dances with little thought for the dancers' special abilities, but moved them about like dolls. To Katherine, the way to plan a dance was to consider the dancers themselves, choosing steps to fit their particular talents.

Katherine began to feel that her own special ability might lie in finding ideas and stories which could be shown in the dance, and then finding ways to express them. Already she was using both ballet and modern dance, for some ideas worked better with modern, others were better with ballet.

Soon after this, Katherine met a young man named

Mark Turbyfill. He was a dancer too, and, like Katherine, interested in choreography.

They found much in common to talk about—not just that first evening, but many times after that. Gradually, out of their talk, a new idea began to take form. Katherine first put it into words.

"There are national ballets," she said. "Almost every country has a ballet company. Wouldn't it be wonderful if we Negroes could have a ballet of our own?"

Mark nodded. "There's the Russian Ballet—the *Ballet Russe*. Why not—"

Katherine interrupted him excitedly. "—the Negro Ballet—the *Ballet Negre!*"

"*Ballet Negre*," Mark repeated, nodding in satisfaction. "Give it the French name, like the *Ballet Russe*. And you know who should start it? We should!"

Katherine agreed. "We should. We can. But we can't do it all by ourselves. Eric Delamarter is a friend of yours. Do you suppose he could help us? If he would, we'd be on our way. Talk to him, Mark, please!"

Katherine and Mark together talked to Eric Delamarter, who was the assistant director of the Chicago Symphony Orchestra. Their enthusiasm for *Ballet Negre* was catching. He quickly agreed to help them establish a school, for every important ballet company has a school of its own.

"What will you teach?" he asked. "Modern and ballet, or—"

Mark shook his head. "Ballet only. Since the *Ballet Russe* is our guide, we think modern dance would be out of place."

Katherine and Mark began to round up students, always keeping their eyes open for talented Negro dancers. Some of their students showed real promise. Better yet, some of them shared Katherine's and Mark's wonderful vision of a Negro ballet. They worked and worked, staff and students alike, preparing for a public performance. But they didn't yet know where or when that performance would take place.

Katherine and Mark were discussing it one day when Mark had a bright idea. "I was talking to the head of the entertainment committee for the Beaux Arts Ball the other day," Mark said. "He's lining up acts to appear at the ball. Katherine, wouldn't that be a wonderful place for the first performance of *Ballet Negre?*"

The Beaux Arts Ball was held once a year. Wealthy and important people came to it. "Mark, that would be perfect!" Katherine said.

"All right. I'll go talk to the fellow I know. You get busy and create the best dances in the world."

Katherine's imagination raced. She spent hours planning and sketching and making notes. She described to the students exactly what she wanted. "Negro Rhapsody" was born, a dance created especially for the ball.

Katherine, Mark, and their dance group worked hard practicing for their very own ballet. Katherine drove her students hard, drove herself harder. "So many people think Negroes can't do anything except the old Negro dances, the cakewalk and the soft shoe. We've got to prove what we *can* do."

The great night arrived. "We're first on the program," Katherine pointed out to Mark. "Isn't that wonderful?"

He shook his head. "It's not a very good place. By the time the program is over, people are likely to forget what came first."

"We will be so good they can't forget us," Katherine promised him. "Come on—it's time."

The *Ballet Negre* company performed "Negro Rhapsody" perfectly. Their performance, and the cheers of the audience, were greater even than Katherine's hopes.

She and Mark exchanged a long, thrilled look as the

clapping called for yet another bow. This was such an important audience. Help for the group and engagements were surely on the way now—success for *Ballet Negre!*

But as the evening wore on, and act followed act, Katherine's enthusiasm grew less, her hopes dimmed. Mark might be right. The acts were all so good! And the audience clapped for each one as loudly and as long as they had clapped for the *Ballet Negre.*

But it was not until the weeks after the Beaux Arts Ball that Katherine allowed herself to believe what was by now so obviously true: the audience had loved the *Ballet Negre* . . . and had promptly forgotten all about it.

They would have to start all over again.

CHAPTER 7

Travel At Last!

"If at first you don't succeed . . ." Katherine said.

"Try again," Albert finished for her. "You'll make it, Katherine. It was just bad luck, the timing of things at the ball. Your *Ballet Negre's* a sound idea."

"Maybe—well, yes, it *is*. I'm sure of that. But it's ahead of its time," Katherine said. "The public just isn't ready for serious Negro dance yet."

All of the *Ballet Negre* group felt discouraged. Gradually they drifted away. Katherine's students were fewer now, too, but expenses kept right on.

To make her slim income stretch farther, Katherine moved to an old stable. It gave her a roof over her head and space for her dancing classes, but little else.

There were bugs in the stable. There was no water. The old furnace gave out with the first cold wave. Katherine couldn't afford to pay for gas. She developed a bad cough. Her students caught cold. Night after night, Katherine went to bed right after supper, crawling under the covers in an attempt to keep warm.

"If I can't get any heat," she told a friend, "I will get sick—I mean *really* sick. I will have to give up dancing. What can I *do?*"

"You just leave everything to me," he said calmly.

The next night he came over and showed her how to break into the city's gas main and draw out gas to be used in the stable.

It was wonderful to be warm again! Katherine loved the simple pleasure of not freezing to death each night. But in the back of her mind, there was a doubt. This wasn't honest. Better than freezing, but still—what would Mother say? Katherine wasn't really surprised when a policeman knocked on the door a few days later.

"Are you the person who lives here?" he asked sternly. When Katherine confessed that she was, he went on, "Well, then, you are under arrest."

Katherine talked hard, feeling desperate. She could sense that the policeman did understand about the cold room, and that he felt sorry for her.

"All right, then, I will let you off this time," he told her. "But that gas supply has to be shut off. And there'll be checks made to be sure it stays shut off."

Katherine felt limp after he was gone. She wasn't in jail, but what would she do now? She couldn't keep on studying, teaching, and then coming home to this cold, battered old stable. She had to do something. Somehow, she had to get students who could pay to come to her classes, so that she could at least afford heat. The ones she had now were as short of cash as she was.

"What you need are older students who won't desert your cause without giving it a fair try," Katherine's own teacher told her.

Katherine nodded. "I thought maybe a new approach, too, maybe modern dance instead of ballet. Do you think—could you help me train my new group? If I can start a new group, that is?"

So Katherine changed the name of her school to the Negro Dance Group. With her teacher, Ludmilla Speranzeva, assisting and advising her, Katherine taught only modern dance. Some interesting themes and beats were developed there, and two programs were given. But, as with *Ballet Negre*, luck seemed against them. Katherine saw her Negro Dance Group fail as the other had.

"I'm gradually finding out that the name of it is one

problem," Katherine told Albert. "The mothers don't like it. They think the children will be taught Negro dancing—you know, dances like our ancestors back in Africa did!"

"Then why not change its name again?" suggested Albert.

"I could, I guess," Katherine agreed. "Might be confusing, but it would beat spending another winter freezing to death. People just can't seem to realize that Negroes can develop their own dance forms, based on birth, youth, age, and death. And there's so much from our own experience that can be added to well-known subjects of literature, art, and music. But how to convince those mothers! Not to mention the other mothers who think I'm too strict and push the kids so hard I'm ruining their natural talents."

Katherine's thoughts were completely switched from these problems by having the ballet mistress of the Chicago Civic Opera ask her to appear in a ballet about the French island of Martinique. With delight, Katherine found herself agreeing to dance not in the chorus, but to be one of the three leads. The ballet was called "Guiablesse," or the Devil Woman. It was thrilling to work with such wonderful dancers, and with the Chicago Symphony Orchestra. Better yet was the knowledge that they thought her good enough to dance a lead role in the ballet!

Katherine's public performance didn't make her famous, but it did attract more students to her school. And it attracted enough interest in her to keep her and her school going.

However, she was still a young student-teacher, and the going was rough. Students came, but other students dropped out. With each class, there were empty places and new faces. The beginning steps had to be taught dozens of times.

"Katherine, your standards are too high," other dancers—white dancers—told her. "Not everyone is as talented or as interested as you are. Your training's too hard. You are holding back your students and ruining their natural talents."

Katherine frowned. "You sound just like the fond mothers! Listen, I've seen enough to know that the greatest enemy of the serious Negro dancer is the idea that he's a natural-born dancer. Negroes are just like anybody else—except that they have to be several times better to succeed. They have to study and practice and work harder than they believe is possible. And the first thing they have to do is forget this old idea they have a special, natural talent! Once they fall into that trap, they stop growing, both as people and as artists. They stop trying and give only fair performances. And then people say that is all you can expect from Negroes!"

Katherine talked about dance and her ideas to whoever would listen. Over and over again, she pointed out that it was important to make a careful study of dance forms, to search for what each individual could do best with the dance. Then patience was needed, and desire, to perfect any talent, any new ideas—through practice and more practice.

It was hard for a girl in her early twenties to keep fighting for an idea. There was not much reward, except the feeling that she was doing the only thing she really wanted to do.

"You are working too hard," Albert said. "You ought to take things easier."

Katherine laughed at him. "With a new dance program coming up? If I take things easy, there won't *be* any program! Though I suppose my usual luck will hold true and somebody will steal the show from us."

"Don't be so gloomy," Albert scolded. "You *are* working too hard, to be talking that way."

Katherine grinned. "Oh, all right. I really do feel hopeful—you know I always do. It's just that I'm afraid to admit it."

Certainly there was nothing about the setting of the new dance program which could raise Katherine's hopes that this time would be different. The only place Katherine could afford to rent was a chilly loft in a part of town not often visited by strangers. Surely only parents and friends would compose the audience. But it was good practice, and Katherine felt pride in her students' ability.

On the night of the program, one of the students called to Katherine to peek through the curtains.

"Guess who that white lady in the audience is!"

Somebody slumming, most likely, Katherine thought —so what?

"She," Katherine was informed, "is Mrs. Alfred Rossenwald Stern. You've heard of the Rosenwald Foundation, haven't you? The organization that gives money to people to study or start new projects in the theater, or art, or the dance? Well! And Mrs. Stern looks as if she likes what she's seen so far!"

Katherine smiled. It was a flattering idea, that her group could impress such a person. But she had impressed people before, and where had it got her?

Only days later, Katherine Dunham opened her mail and found an invitation to come to the board room of the Rosenwald Foundation. Mrs. Stern *had* been impressed, then! Nervously, Katherine prepared for the interview. What should she wear? Would they just talk to her, or did they want to see her dance? At last,

Katherine put on a jacket and skirt over practice tights and carried her dancing shoes along in a bag. She was prepared for anything.

Now it was Katherine's turn to be impressed. All by itself, the board room had a solid air of importance. The professors and other board members were certainly men and women of education and excellent background. And they were interested in her work!

"Just what study, Miss Dunham, would you suggest that you follow?" a board member asked, after they had all talked to her for a while. "With the understanding, of course, that we finance it?"

"It's a bit difficult to put into words," Katherine replied slowly. Difficult, indeed! She was so thrilled she could hardly speak, that was all! "Do you mind if I show you?"

Lucky that she *had* worn tights and brought dancing shoes! Quickly, she changed, removing her street clothes. Then Katherine stood straight in her dancing clothes. She looked directly at the board members, smiling a bit.

"This," she said, "is the kind of dancing that is taught in Chicago—in most dancing schools everywhere, I suppose."

She did some pretty steps and turns. She pretended she was a fawn, and then a girl in love.

Pausing, she explained, "What I want to do is to find something more alive—something that will help me teach people about Negroes. Help me teach Negroes about themselves, their orgins."

She did a short, African dance which she had created. If only she had the proper music to accompany her! Did it look the way it should, or would the effect fall flat?

Hoping for the best, when it ended, Katherine said, "That's what I'm after. I want to find out *why* Africans dance like that. How they started. And what this kind of dancing does to people, the life they lead."

Katherine listened closely to the discussion that followed. It sounded as if they were in favor of helping her realize her dream.

Then the board voted—and their decision was that they would give Katherine Dunham a Julius Rosenwald Traveling Fellowship for anthropological research! She would travel for a year in the West Indies, which they felt was an especially rich area for her research.

Katherine was trembling with excited happiness. The West Indies—the Caribbean Islands! Why, that was one of her long-time dreams. There'd be all those mysterious ceremonies to study.

Katherine heard the members of the board talking to her, but already she was imagining the islands she would visit. As each member stepped forward to shake her hand and wish her luck, she could hardly answer, she was so eager to set off.

She, Katherine Dunham, from the South Side slums and a Joliet dry cleaning shop, was now going to discover the true sources of dance beat and movement! How could she stand still and make light conversation when there was so much to do?

CHAPTER 8

Accompong

"And in my innocent way, I thought once they gave me that Traveling Fellowship, I'd better get right home and pack so I could hop on the first train to catch the boat for the West Indies!" Katherine said, laughing.

"Not that easy, huh?" Albert asked.

Katherine sighed, but her eyes shone. "I should say not. You don't win it one day and go tearing off to the ends of the earth the next. Why, right now I'm getting special training at Northwestern University to prepare me."

"That's something!"

Katherine nodded. "There's so much to learn, I

91

sometimes wonder if I will ever get to go. I may die of old age first." Ticking it off on her fingers, she recited, "I have to learn how to approach strangers and live among them. What to look for that has meaning for the anthropologist. How to make up reports of what I observe. How to handle cameras, recordings and motion-picture equipment. And, Albert, did you know that in the tropics, mold can destroy film and recordings? Anyhow, it's awfully important for me to learn how to take care of equipment."

Albert nodded with understanding. "Yes, because if anything got destroyed, it would be the very thing you couldn't replace."

Dr. Herskovits, at Northwestern University, was the most helpful teacher Katherine had ever had. She listened closely to everything he told her as he showed her how an anthropologist works in the field. He became her good friend. Dr. Herskovits was the first to advise her to visit Accompong in Jamaica, where she would find the last of a tribe of people called "Maroons."

"The Maroons of Jamaica have an unusual history," Dr. Herskovits told Katherine. "They ran wild for centuries, first under the Spaniards, then under the English. The mountains protected them from their enemies and from civilization. Now only a few live in this one tiny village called Accompong. They continue to observe the ceremonies and customs of their native West Africa, where the Spaniards captured their ancestors.

Finally it was time to leave. Katherine had her clothes and equipment packed, her trip planned. The first stop would be Haiti, then Jamaica, then the island of Martinique, and last Trinidad.

"It's a good start," she said to herself. "Some day later on I can get to Africa!"

Katherine's stop in Haiti was a short one, for she had made up her mind to get to Jamaica and the Maroons as fast as possible. The sooner she was started on her research, the better.

Even in Haiti, people told strange stories about the natives of Accompong. When Katherine landed in Jamaica and mentioned where she was going, the Jamaicans had more tales of the wild music and dancing of the mountain tribe. They could hardly believe that a pretty American girl was actually going up into the Maroon country, and they tried to discourage her. The natives of Accompong, people told her, had never had a visitor who stayed longer than a day. Their language was a difficult mixture of Creole and English.

However, the more stories she heard, the more interested Katherine became. The Maroons sounded wonderful! Frightening, yes, but certainly a rich source of primitive customs. "But will I be able to understand them?" Katherine asked herself. "And will they be able to understand me?"

Katherine boarded a small train that climbed and wound its way far up into the mountains. It stopped in a town called Maggotty, where Katherine got off and was met by "the Colonel," a wrinkled little man wearing a worn sun helmet. He drove her from Maggotty to Whitehall in an old, battered car.

During the drive, Katherine was puzzled by his references to "the beasts." At Whitehall she discovered that "the beasts" were to be her transportation for the rest of the trip—mules!

Katherine didn't trust her saddle, which slipped from side to side on her mule as they followed the narrow, muddy path. They passed tangled forests of banana and bread fruit trees. She held on to the neck of her "beast" and closed her eyes to sudden deep cliffs dropping away into nowhere.

Ahead of them, natives trotted barefooted and half-naked, carrying Katherine's trunks and equipment balanced on their heads. Natives, mules, and trail climbed up, down and steeply up again, at dizzying angles.

Katherine held her breath—and thought how nice it would be to be back in flat, noisy Chicago.

At last they stopped before a tiny house perched on the edge of the mountain. Far below, Katherine could see the town of Kingston. This house belonged to the Colonel. He was the Maroon chief, she now learned.

Katherine was to sleep at the Colonel's house. That left one other bed and two rooms for the Colonel, his wife, two daughters, a son, a son-in-law and several grandchildren. Katherine was glad to hear that the Colonel hoped to find her a house of her own very soon.

It had been a long day, and Katherine was hungry. The sweet, roasted bread fruit was delicious. After they had eaten, Katherine went to take some of her things from her trunk. Her hosts spotted the precious record player, and they insisted on having it turned on. For hours she sat up with the family, listening to records, and trying to hide the fact that she was sleepy.

Any other time, Katherine would have enjoyed the records as much as her new Maroon friends did, but she was tired and worried. She was here for a purpose, to learn about the Maroons and their dances and culture. Would the tables be turned? Would they learn more about her than she would about them?

When Katherine woke the next morning, the Colonel

was pacing up and down outside, anxious to see her. While she slept, he had been arranging for a place for her to live. There was a spare house in Accompong. This was most unusual, the Colonel pointed out, for by tradition, a Maroon owns only what he can use himself. But Katherine was lucky.

Practical matters taken care of, the Colonel led Katherine to his back porch. It was little more than a cat walk hanging over a steep cliff. There she and the village chief held their first official conversation, discussing the dances Katherine had come to study and take part in, especially the Koromantee war dances. And they talked of the Maroons.

The Maroons had come, at first, from the most fierce tribes of West Africa, the Colonel told Katherine. The Spaniards never succeeded in making "good" slaves of these proud, independent people. When the English drove the Spaniards from Jamaica in the 1600's, fifteen hundred Negroes and Mulattoes fled to the hills, where they lived by hunting wild hogs and raiding small villages. Slaves who had run away joined them from time to time. In 1690, slaves in Jamaica rebelled, and many more escaped to the mountains.

By then, the black tribes in the mountains were called "Maroons." Some say the name came from the Spanish word, "marrano," meaning "hog hunter." It could also be a short form of "cimarrón," the Spanish word for "wild."

The British had sent scouting parties up into the hills to capture the Maroons. Most of the British were killed in the mountain passes. Only a few returned, telling horrible tales of black magic, walking forests, and fierce warriors who attacked and vanished into the hills in the space of one moment.

The British finally used everything they had to break up the Maroons. The strength of the mountain tribes was at last destroyed. By 1835 there were only 60 Maroon families left in Accompong, eight in Moore Town, ten in Charleston and 20 in Scott Hall.

"And today there are only the Maroons of Accompong?" Katherine asked her host.

Sadly, the Colonel nodded.

Katherine noticed that while she and the Colonel were talking, curious people had stopped to look at her. The same thing happened when she took a walk the next morning. But she was puzzled. The Maroons seemed to appear and disappear for no reason. She felt as if many secrets divided her from these people. Katherine thought she could sense the drums somewhere in the distance—somewhere she might never be allowed to go.

The Colonel took Katherine to see the "spare" house

which was now hers. It had a straw roof like the other houses, and the kitchen was in the back yard, its dirt floor packed smooth by bare feet. The cooking was done in black iron pots over an open fire on the ground. Outside were coffee vines, with tiny white flowers, and one bush entirely covered with beautiful pink blossoms. The sweet, heavy perfume of the flowers made everything around her seem like a dream world to Katherine.

At the top of Katherine's list of places to see was the "parade." It was located on the highest hill in Accompong, and that was where council meetings were held, and feasts and weddings, and town dances.

The Colonel was polite, but not very encouraging, about the dances Katherine was so eager to see. "Patience," she told herself. "I must have patience, and win their confidence first."

And then one afternoon a girl ran up to Katherine, bursting with excitement. "A dance! Tonight! The man with the fiddle has come from Whitehall!"

As dusk fell, a steady procession from the valley and the hills began moving up the cliff to the parade. Katherine carried her movie camera, wondering if there'd be enough light to use it, for the only light in the black tropic night came from lanterns and candles.

On the parade, rum was already being passed

around. Everybody was feeling gay—except the man with the fiddle, who complained about his fee. He banged his tin cup for more rum. He gazed at the heavens. He did everything but play his fiddle.

Katherine studied the crowd. Most of the people had dark brown skins, but some were very black. Old or young, all were slender with strong, solid muscles. Women of all ages—even tiny children—wore loose cotton dresses tied at the waist and falling well below the knee. They wore clean white scarves on their heads. The men had on jeans or tan trousers, and straw hats. A few of them wore short, loose coats especially for the occasion. Except for council members, and young men who wished to make an impression on the girls, everyone was barefoot.

They greeted each other in their soft voices.

"Cousin, ha' you dis ev'nin'?"

"Me well, Mars' Teddy."

"Howdy, Uncle."

"Ev'nin', Godbrother."

"Ev'nin', Nana."

The ladies, even the young ones, seemed to like being addressed as "Mam." Men used "Godbrother," and "Marsa," and "Baba," or "Brother" when they greeted friends of their own age. "Uncle" and "Nana" were terms of respect for older people.

After a few more cups of rum, the man who played the fiddle was finally ready. While he warmed up on snatches of old English airs and Creole tunes, the men hurried to find partners. Two lines formed, men in one, women in the other. Then the starting notes of the music were struck and the dance began.

Katherine had heard that there would be "set" dances tonight, and she was interested to find that the set dance was the Accompong form of the old quadrille, a French square dance popular at the court of Napoleon. Even more interesting than the dance itself were the dancers. Most of them were well into their seventies, and the old women of the village were the most popular partners—all evening long! The Colonel's favorite was a small, bent lady, whose scarf kept slipping away from the gray knots of her hair. She took his arm with great pride. She knew she was the best dancer in Accompong.

Every now and then there was time out. After each break, the dancing grew wilder and freer. The men no longer gave the ladies sweeping bows. Instead, they leaped to the center of the square with heels clicking high in the air. They did back bends and fancy turns, and the women joined in. Their eyes shone, their steps were high and light. Bare black legs flashed in the lantern light as partners changed more quickly. The fiddle player thumped his foot and bow, keeping up with the dancers' pounding feet.

The last figure of the set dance was the shay-shay. As it was about to begin, the Colonel pulled Katherine to her feet. Suddenly she could think of nothing but the strong hip movements and the beat of the music. She felt herself dance as she never had before. She was free! She was finding the true sources of beat and movement!

Hours later, the young American was completely worn out. Through the fog of smoking lanterns she could see that the old women were still dancing wildly. They looked stronger than ever. How did they do it?

"In Kingston, or in America," Katherine thought, "couples would be clinging to each other, dead tired! But the Maroons—dancing seems a part of them! They have the thrill of a perfect art form." Katherine vowed to herself that, back home, with her next dance group, the Maroon quadrille would be a must.

CHAPTER 9

War Dance

Katherine had two visitors the next day—Priscilla, the Colonel's granddaughter, and Old Maria, who was very old indeed. Her joints were stiff, and she was bent over nearly in half. Old Maria had been told that the "pretty Missus" had danced the night before. Now she wanted to hear all about it. So Katherine put on a show for her, pretending to be one of the men approaching a lady, and then kicking up her heels in a few of the steps of the quadrille.

Old Maria laughed until she almost choked. Then she took Priscilla by the hand, and together they showed Katherine many other dance steps. As they danced, Katherine hoped she could remember all the steps so she could teach them at home. Watching them, Katherine also thought about how well the young and old got along in Accompong.

Now that the ice was broken, groups of people often came to Katherine's house at night. There were always a few of the very old, and some of the very young, along with young men and women and middle-aged parents.

Katherine was disappointed to find that there were almost no artists in Accompong. Oh, there were a few exceptions—beautiful wooden basins were still being carved from the trunks of cedar trees, and some of the natives still made lovely sleeping mats from marsh reeds or banana leaves.

One of the oldest men in the village even twisted bark from the lace bark tree into rope and knotted it in interesting patterns to form hammocks. Katherine asked him to make her one, and hoped that it would be done by the time she was ready to go home. In the back of her mind she was planning a new dance. The hammock would be an important part of it.

Katherine also had a good friend, Ba' Weeyums, make her a tambourine. Another friend, Ba' Foster, was making her a goombay—a small square drum patterned on an ancient one which had been used in battle. These were very special favors. Not many people played musical instruments any more, and even fewer remembered how to make them.

The Maroons had always used a horn called the abeng to announce deaths and to call special meetings at the parade. But they told Katherine that Galleo, the best horn blower, had died last year. The new horn blower had yet learned how to play very well. The abeng being used in Accompong was made of deer horn, and it had come down through the centuries from the first Maroon chief, Juan de Bolas. It was believed that he or his ancestors brought it over from Africa.

When the abeng was played, the blower talked into a long opening on the side of the horn. He controlled the tone by placing his thumb at a small hole on the tip of the horn. Then he would speak actual words into the horn, or a secret code of signals known only to Maroons. The "talking messages" of an expert horn blower could be understood by Maroons 24 miles away.

There was a second abeng in the village. It had been made in 1665. Its keeper was Ba' Reed, and Katherine hoped he would come to trust her enough to give her his abeng. She had already acquired the last remaining gourd rattle and a bamboo flute. With the goombay, the tambourine and the abeng, she would have a complete collection of Maroon musical instruments.

Once in a while Ba' Weeyums or the Colonel's dancing partner, Mis' Mary, would consent to talk into Katherine's recording machine. Katherine wanted very much to share the rich humor of the Maroons with people at home, and even in other parts of the world. She remembered what Dr. Herskovits had taught her about mold, and now, more than ever, she realized how hard it would be to replace a ruined recording.

Of course, dancing was another Maroon art. By now, Katherine knew the steps to the set dances. Ever since the night on the parade, Ba' Weeyums, a friend of his named Ba' Teddy, Mis' Mary, and others had gone over the figures with her, time and again. They came evening after evening to teach her in her little house.

But Katherine worried about the Koromantee songs and dances—the war dances. She could not leave Accompong without seeing them, and time was getting so short! The Colonel kept putting her off. He made promises, but it was clear that he did not mean to arrange a Koromantee evening. As a modern chief, he was trying to do away with all of the old African traditions. Katherine had a feeling he was jealous of her friendship with Ba' Weeyums and Ba' Teddy, too.

When Katherine asked the village people about the

dances, some said the Colonel had forbidden them. Others said they had been forgotten long ago. Some even said there was no goombay, and nobody left to play it even if there *was* one.

Katherine knew that the dances still existed. "If I can't gain the confidence of these people enough to get them to show me these dances, I'm a failure as an anthropologist," Katherine told herself sadly. "I don't even know if there's any point in going on to the other islands. If I fail here, I will fail everywhere, and I'd just be wasting the Foundation's money."

Then one night she heard music coming from the hills—music that had to be Koromantee songs! The sound was not like anything she had heard before. Shrill, wild notes and low, sad ones came strongly to her eager ears.

"Mis' Mattie Cross died this morning," Katherine reminded herself. "This must be connected with her funeral."

Realizing that this might be the chance she had been waiting for, Katherine quickly grabbed her equipment and set out for the hills.

When she got there, Katherine could see Ba' Wee-yums, a lantern in one hand and a bottle of rum in the other, leading the men who were digging the grave in a Koromantee song, and a few steps of a dance.

"Chali Kotta man-di!" he shouted.

"Ho 'nansi, Wa ee bo!" the chorus answered.

Everyone was covered with yellow mud, a mixture of sweat and clay from the grave. They hung over an opening in the earth, falling down now and then and changing places to dig, but continuing the song.

Katherine peered into the grave. By the light of the lantern, she saw that the usual hole had been dug. But now they were digging at the back of the grave, extending the hole under the ground they were standing on.

"It looks just like the tunnel grave of the Bush Negroes of Dutch Guiana," Katherine thought with a thrill. At Northwestern, Dr. Herskovits had told her about this kind of grave. It was one of his special interests. This was marvelous! African and South American African traditions were meeting right here in Jamaica. And she, Katherine Dunham, had discovered it!

In the tunnel grave it would be impossible—according to the folklore—for the lively spirit of Mis' Mattie Cross to bring back her body if she chose to return from the dead. Only her spirit could escape the trap of the tunnel grave. Her body would remain under the earth.

The ceremony was over. There would be no more

singing. This taste of Koromantee made Katherine hopeful—and restless—for more. She had to remind herself over and over to be patient.

By now, living with the Maroons, Katherine had changed a great many of her ways. She no longer boiled her drinking water. She didn't bother to watch while her food was being prepared, and she ate and drank what was served her. She even decided that red ashes and cold water were as good a way as any to clean pots and dishes.

She put away her American creams and powders, and learned to rub coconut oil into her skin to protect it from the tropic sun. She began wearing the sack-like dresses of the Accompong women, and she practiced carrying tins of water on her head. She was marking time until, if ever, a lucky break brought more Koromantee into her reach. She was learning to live as if she, too, were a Maroon.

Katherine admired the people of Accompong. She liked their lively spirit and good humor and the kindness which they showed to one another, and to her. To pay them back in a small way, Katherine planned a feast for the village.

Since fresh meat was rare, she arranged to have pig cooked over coals, and goat stewed in large iron kettles. Bread was a luxury, too, so there would be loaves and loaves of bread. And there would be platters of rice and corn and bread fruit. Pineapples, bananas, and plenty of rum. And, to top it off, cake baked in an iron pot buried in hot ashes.

The feast was a great success. Every bit of food disappeared, and the rum inspired stories and laughter. When it was all over, they played cricket and other games on the parade, and danced until dawn. The fiddle player was in excellent form. Katherine joined in the dances until the long day began to catch up with her. Finally she slipped away, back to her little house, stretched out in bed and fell asleep.

At last Katherine had to pack. She must leave for Martinique, with or without the Koromantee war dances. She gathered together the things that she would take with her. The woven hammock was here, and the tambourine, the flute, and a small bowl of cedar wood. But where was the goombay? Ba' Foster had promised it for yesterday.

She decided to walk down to Ba' Foster's place to find out about the delay. It was dusk. As she stepped out, two mouse-bats dived past her head, and Katherine shivered. But disgust changed to excitement, as she sensed something in the air—something which made her move fast and catch her breath. The sound of a drum! Only a goat skin drawn tight over hollowed-out wood and beaten by a black palm could produce that sound, surely. It was the sound she had been trying to catch up with all this time!

Ba' Foster's yard and house were empty. But down in a valley, behind a stand of bread fruit trees, Katherine spotted a flicker of light. The drum beat was clear and expert, with quick changes from long to short, low to high, and loud to soft.

Then she spotted the eager bodies standing in a circle. Twenty Maroons, old and young, eyes gleaming in the light, watched Mis' Mary and an old man perform a strange dance. Ba' Weeyums leaned over the goombay—*her* goombay!—sliding his palm along the skin of the drum.

They were all there—Ba' Teddy, Ba' Foster. They had betrayed her. They were going to have a Koromantee dance, and they hadn't invited her!

One of them saw her. "Ev'nin', Missus."

Katherine had tears in her eyes but she replied, "Ev'nin'."

Ba' Foster came up to her, the goombay under his arm. "I was jus' going to deliver eem to you," he said. "I was on my way when I meet Ba' Weeyums. Ba' Weeyums ask to play eem jus' dis once."

Katherine didn't believe one word. She looked at

Ba' Weeyums. "I must forget that I feel betrayed. This is the moment I've been waiting for. This is my last chance for the Koromantee dances."

Even as she stood thinking, the circle around them was shrinking. Half of the Maroons had already slipped away into the darkness. "Everyone's going!" Katherine cried.

"De goombay eem good 'nuf, but eem need rum," Ba' Weeyums told her. "Goombay don' talk good till eem have rum."

Rum! Katherine sent one of the young men to fetch a jug. She and Ba' Weeyums faced one another again. Why hadn't he told her that he was an expert with the drum? He assured her that he would have beaten the drum for her any time. There just hadn't been a drum to beat.

Ba' Teddy said that the Colonel would be furious if he knew what was going on. He had warned everybody not to do these dances while Katherine was in the village. The evening had not been planned, it had just happened. People passing by had heard the drum, and the word had spread. Even this could not have happened if the Colonel had been home. But he was miles away, on a trip to Maggotty.

"I won't tell anybody," Katherine promised. "But

please go on—only to break in the goombay," she pleaded.

The rum arrived. Ba' Weeyums poured some on the face of the drum, rubbed it, and raised the jug to his own lips. He spat rum on the drum. All the while, he muttered away in what Katherine knew must be Koromantee. He poured a few drops of rum on the ground. The spirit of the drum was now happy, he explained, as he bent over it once more.

To Katherine, it seemed that the drum came alive. The tone sounded fuller than before. Perhaps Ba' Weeyums was right—some Gold Coast god had been listening!

Gradually, the people came back to the circle. The rum was handed around as the dancers began again. Ba' Teddy explained the dance to Katherine. Mis' Mary was an evil spirit, the "duppy" of a dead woman who once worked black magic. The old man was the "doctor," determined to get the duppy into his power.

Ba' Weeyums led a song in Koromantee. The women answered. The duppy circled the doctor. The doctor advanced toward her. Then she pursued him. The doctor shook in fear before this woman he had raised from the dead, his arms thrown wide, fingers wide apart, hands trembling. Mis' Mary's face was like a

mask. Her body seemed to flow. She leaned over
him. . . .

And Ba' Teddy raised his hand. Drum and song
stopped. The air was heavy with the quick breathing of
the dancers.

"Dat dance bad dance," Ba' Teddy muttered.

Katherine started to speak.

"Be' ax no questions, missus. Me don't see dat for
long time. Dat mix up wid bad biznuss. Better ef
missus fergit."

Forget? Katherine knew she would remember it all
her life. She had read descriptions of such dances, but
they were nothing to the real thing!

Swiftly, the mood of drum and dance changed. Two
men hopped around in a circle, as if in a cock fight.
They were good actors, and the audience howled with
laughter.

Katherine asked to see a Koromantee war dance next.
It was the dance the drunk men had attempted the
night of Mis' Mattie Cross's death. First the dancers
walked around stiffly, looking like people warming up
for a race. Then there was a lively step which reminded Katherine of an Irish dance. Since war dances
were performed by both men and women, Katherine
soon joined.

The songs were in Koromantee. One woman shook a

rattle, keeping time to the drumming. The dancing couples waved sticks and scarves in the air. Then the couples parted and there was a confusion of leaping, shouting warriors. Bush fighting against an enemy followed. Mis' Mary grabbed Katherine by the shoulders and shook her hard. She had become a woman of the old days, working the men up to battle pitch.

When the dancing was over, the goombay was Katherine's. With Ba' Teddy and Ba' Weeyums she walked up the hill, exhausted.

"Now I can leave," Katherine murmured to herself with deep satisfaction. "I've learned the Koromantee dances. I'm not a failure as an anthropologist after all!"

CHAPTER 10

Which Career?

Katherine had one fear about the time she spent in the West Indies—that everyone would have forgotten her by the time she came back home.

Before she went away, she had made many valuable friends in the world of the dance in Chicago. Now that she was back, would she have to start all over again?

Instead, as it turned out, she had become—well, not exactly famous but much better known than she had been before. The reports that she had sent back to the Rosenwald Foundation had been well received. The letters she had written friends in Chicago had been shown to friends of the friends. Now it seemed, everyone knew who Katherine Dunham was and what she could do.

"It's a wonderful feeling," she told Albert. "I wondered if I'd be able to find a job. And instead I have so many offers I don't know which job to choose!"

Albert nodded. "It's almost like a miracle. Dance companies and dance directors everywhere seem to know about you. They are more interested than ever because of what you learned and brought back from the West Indies."

"It's not just the field of the dance," she told him. "For instance, here's this offer from the Chicago City Theater. They want me to head a writers' project that will study cultures. Remember, I wasn't sure when you suggested anthropology to me that it was what I wanted?"

"Are you going to accept the offer?" Albert wanted to know. "After all, it's writing, not dancing."

"I know. But I want to do it all the same. I'm interested in writing, too, you know. And I'll have plenty of time to spare for dancing. I'd like to try teaching something else—find out if I can do it."

And so she went to work on the project. It did seem strange to be teaching something other than dancing, but she quickly got used to it. As she had told Albert, she had plenty of time for dancing, and for teaching dance, and she made the most of it. Her year in the West Indies had given her enough ideas for new dances to last a life time. She tried to do all she possibly could while the memories of Accompong were fresh in her mind. She worked very hard on the choreography for many dances, and students in her classes tried them out and worked on them with her.

Word of these exciting, new, and different dance forms spread around, and led to another offer for Katherine. The Federal Theater of Chicago asked her to plan and produce a full-length ballet that would make use of this material.

Honored, Katherine agreed, although this meant that now her time would be very full and she would have to work very hard. "But I love hard work," she told Albert, "and this will be the best show case ever for my West Indies dances. Who knows what it might lead to?"

"Maybe even New York," Albert told her. She shook her head. "That's too much to hope for," she said. "But at least it will get me known by everyone who matters here in Chicago."

Katherine began to plan the new ballet. What should it be based on? In her mind she saw the islands she had visited, saw again the dances that had delighted her. A lot—perhaps her whole future career—depended on this ballet she was going to plan and produce. It had to be marvelous, had to stir everyone who saw it.

At last she made up her mind. Taking a pad of paper, she began to draw on it, planning one dance, then another.

The result was "L'Ag'ya," inspired by a dramatic dance of the island of Martinique. And, from the first performance, it was a greater success than Katherine had dared to hope!

And, just as Albert had guessed, the success of "L'Ag'ya" brought Katherine not one, but two offers from New York.

"But not exactly the most exciting kinds of offers," she told her brother, looking as if she didn't know whether to laugh or cry. "This one is an invitation to put on an evening of Negro Dance at the 94th Street YMHA—a YMHA, for goodness' sake!"

Albert grinned. "Listen, don't knock it. Maybe it's only a YMHA, but it's a *New York* YMHA, isn't it? It's a step in the right direction. Anyway, you said you had two offers. What's the other one?"

"The International Ladies' Garment Workers Union is going to put on a show called *Pins and Needles*. I've been asked to be the dance director of it. But Albert, that doesn't sound like much, either. After all, it will not be a professional production. It may not be up to New York standards. It may not be up to *my* standards!"

"Never mind," Albert told her. "Take both offers and be glad of them. They will get you to New York, at least, and New York is *the* city for anyone with show business ambitions, isn't it?"

"It is indeed. I have done well in Chicago, but if I want to get to the top, New York is the place. All right, I'll go. If anyone does, I ought to know how one thing always leads to another. Maybe these two little shows in New York will lead to a big one."

When Katherine asked around among her friends, she learned that New York's 94th Street YMHA had brought many dancers and writers to the attention of the professional world. So she started for the big city with high hopes, after all.

New York itself was all that Katherine had expected of it—a city of excitement and promise, the heart of the show business world. The evening at the YMHA was wonderful and drew a large audience. And *Pins and Needles* turned out to be very professional indeed. It was a hit, one of the best shows in years, and delighted the New York audiences.

Social life turned out to be wonderful, too. Many of

Katherine's Chicago friends had moved to New York, and through them she made new acquaintances. She was never lonely from the time she arrived.

One of these new acquaintances was John Pratt, a handsome white man who designed stage sets and costumes. It seemed that wherever Katherine went, John Pratt would soon appear—whether by accident or not, she didn't know, or care.

Katherine enjoyed talking to John Pratt. He was interested in a dancer's problems. His costumes didn't interfere with the ability to dance. Some of the men and women who designed costumes didn't understand the problems, and created things that were not at all practical, that got in the way of a dancer's movements.

But their conversation wasn't all about costumes, or even all about the theater. It seemed to Katherine that she could discuss anything with John Pratt, talk to him more freely and easily than she had ever been able to with anyone. She even felt that he could help her with the big problem that now faced her: what should she do next?

"Sometimes I wonder," Katherine told John, "whether I should keep on trying to dance and plan dances, and at the same time continue to work on anthropology. Dancing, choreography, anthropology—all three at once seem like too much to keep up with. Should I try to keep my mind on just one?"

"You are established in all three fields," John pointed out. "It would be a shame to give up any of them."

"Yes, but if I spread myself too thin," Katherine objected, "I might not do well in any of the three."

"Which one would you want most to keep on with?" John asked. Katherine shook her head. She honestly didn't know.

John thought for a few moments. Then he went on slowly. "You might consider this, if you are really serious about giving up one field: you won't have too many years as a dancer. Anthropology, even choreography, you can do all your life, even when you are old. But these are your best years as a dancer."

Katherine nodded. "That idea has been in my mind, too. If I'm going to dance, it has to be now. And right now I'm in demand as a dancer. Perhaps it would be best to stick to my dancing, and to planning steps for dancing, since they're so closely related. Then, later, when I'm past my prime as a dancer, I could concentrate on anthropology."

She smiled at John. "Later on, too, I'll travel again— live among people in far-off corners of the world, so I can bring their dances to audiences everywhere."

"You'll do that, too," John agreed. His eyes and

Katherine's met in a long look. Then he grinned and added, "You'll do that—and I will design your sets and costumes!"

The next time Katherine and John met, she had some wonderful news to tell him. "I'm going to be in *Cabin in the Sky* with Ethel Waters. And George Balanchine is doing the choreography. Just imagine!"

It was enough to thrill any young dancer—an offer to appear, along with the dance group that she had formed a short while ago, in a new musical comedy with the great Negro star. And she would be working with the wonderful Russian dancer and choreographer, George Balanchine.

"Is it a good role?" John asked.

"Oh, is it! I'm going to be a very wicked girl named Georgia Brown. And John—I'm even going to sing! Won't that be something?"

"I don't know. I've never heard you sing," he teased. Then he turned serious. "Katherine, this won't interfere with the dance recital you've been planning, will it?"

She shook her head. "There will be plenty of time to get the dance program over before I get too involved with *Cabin in the Sky*. But I'll have to get busy on it right away. Don't forget, you are designing the costumes and sets. You promised!"

John smiled at her. "And I intend to keep my promise. West Indian dances, right? Latin American Negro-Spanish and Indian dances. And what else?"

"Well, I thought I'd do one called *Br'er Rabbit and de Tar Baby*," Katherine said. "I loved the way my father told that story when I was a little girl."

Shows cost money, and Katherine was glad John was such a good friend. Otherwise, she could not have afforded anyone of such talent as his to design her sets and costumes. There would be expenses enough anyway. She would have to spend all her salary from her new job as dance director for the Labor Stage. Costumes, sets, renting the Windsor Theater—those were only the beginning of the costs.

But when the recital came off, the way it was received made all the work and expenses worth while. The review in the New York *Herald Tribune* said, "Last night Katherine Dunham broke the bonds that have chained the dancing Negro to the . . . white race and introduced us to a dance worthy of her own people. Miss Dunham is the first pioneer of the Negro Dance."

The New York *Times* was equally pleased. The review said that with the arrival of Katherine Dunham, prospects for the development of a Negro dance art looked bright. "If the Negro is to develop an art of his own," the reviewer went on, "he can begin only with the seeds of that art that lie within him—discovering his own roots."

Katherine was delighted. Not only did the men who reviewed the show for the newspapers like what she was doing, they *understood* what she was doing.

The dances—Katherine had named them "Tropics" and "Le Jazz Hot"—had been planned as a single program. But the success of the recital and the rave reviews inspired several more New York performances. The show even took Katherine back home to Chicago, where she and her company played a short engagement at the Hotel Sherman supper club. After that, the show played for a month in California.

"Pretty good," Katherine thought warmly, "for what started out to be only a one-evening performance!"

With all that traveling around, Katherine was kept very busy. Even so, she missed New York. It had come to be, in a short time, like home to her. Besides, New York was where John Pratt lived—and yes, she admitted to herself, she missed John very much indeed.

So, when the engagement in California was over, she was glad to return to New York. She settled down to practice for *Cabin in the Sky*, along with the rest of the cast. Even though the practicing took many hours each day, Katherine found time to work on planning a new dance, which she called "Rites de Passage." And, of course, she found time to spend with John.

Then came an invitation that took Katherine's breath away. She was asked if she would lecture to a faculty audience at Yale University! Indeed she would. Her subject was "An Anthropological Approach to the Theater." Thank goodness, her dance group was ready with "Rites de Passage." She would take the group along to illustrate the points of her lecture. The dance was concerned with two important events in human life, growing up and finding a mate.

The lecture was a great success. "Rites de Passage" was wildly cheered by the audience at Yale. (Later it was banned in Boston!)

Katherine's own performances, plus her very real success when *Cabin in the Sky* opened, attracted considerable attention. Like many talented people who attract attention on Broadway, Katherine got offers to come to Hollywood.

Within the next year, Katherine appeared in three movies—*Carnival of Rhythm, Star-Spangled Banner,* and *Stormy Weather.* Then she was asked to create special dances for a fourth movie, *Pardon My Sarong.*

Katherine found that creating the dances was no problem. Her head was still filled—and always would be—with dance steps and patterns. But the costumes were a real problem. Person after person came up with costumes that looked marvelous as sketches but were total failures when made.

"Why," Katherine wondered in despair, "can't the people who design costumes realize that the dancers have to *move?* Dancers are supposed to be able to *dance!*"

John Pratt understood that. She never needed to worry about the costumes he created for her dancers. But these! Katherine cast a disgusted look around the room, which was heaped with costumes, half-finished, and set aside because they wouldn't work.

She was, Katherine knew, gaining a reputation for being difficult to work with. But all she wanted were costumes that were practical as well as attractive. Surely that wasn't too much to ask?

"Get me John Thomas Pratt," Katherine pleaded at last. "He knows the kinds of costumes I need."

So John came out to Hollywood. He made over the expensive but useless costumes into just what Katherine needed, and drew glowing reviews of his own when the movie was seen.

By now, Katherine had rented an ocean-front home and settled down for a stay in Hollywood.

Altogether, that year was a very wonderful one for Katherine. Broadway, Hollywood, triumphs as a dancer, as a choreographer, even as a singer. Her world had grown to a size she had never dreamed possible. Everything, everything was going right for her.

A wonderful year . . . and something else was to happen that would make it a perfect year.

Katherine and John arranged their work so that they could have a few free days. They went to Mexico for a small, private wedding and a brief, glorious wedding trip.

CHAPTER 11

Home Is a Hotel

The next years Katherine and John spent in constant travel, as the Dunham Dance Company toured the world. And, it seemed to Katherine, they were in constant trouble of one sort or another.

There was the trouble in South America—in São Paulo, Brazil. Rooms had been reserved for the whole company at a fine hotel across the street from the theater where the group would be performing. But when they arrived, they were told there were no rooms.

"You reserved rooms? There must be some mistake. The hotel is full," the man behind the desk told Katherine.

Rooms were located in another hotel on the far side

of the city, but the long trip back and forth across town was a bother. Then John and Katherine were told that the first hotel did have rooms, had had them all along.

"Let's look into that," John said to Miss Scott, the handsome English woman who was Katherine's secretary. "We aren't needed here at practice. Let's go across the street and see what we can find out."

John thought he knew the reason they had been told that the hotel was full. He wanted to test it.

First Miss Scott went to the desk. "Yes, indeed," the manager told her. "We have a room for you."

Then John tried. Yes, there was a room for Mr. Pratt, too.

"And for Katherine Dunham," John added.

The manager was shocked. "Oh, no—she can't stay here!"

He had been right, John told himself. He had suspected that they had been turned away because Katherine was a Negro. But there was supposed to be no racial discrimination—no difference in treatment because of race or color—anywhere in Brazil.

"Is it because of her color?" John asked. His voice was very quiet, his blue eyes like steel.

"Yes," said the manager, who was, himself, much

darker than light-skinned Katherine. "It is impossible. She cannot stay in the Grande Hotel."

Miss Scott and John Pratt went to a lawyer. This was impossible, they were told. There was no color bar in Brazil. "What can I say to you?" the lawyer wanted to know. "Even if this man at the hotel has kept Miss Dunham out, he has broken no law. There is no law against racial discrimination—because there is no discrimination!"

Finally, Miss Scott and John Pratt made the man understand that something must be done.

The lawyer thought about it. At last he smiled and nodded. "There is no provision in civil law to cover this situation," he said. "But criminal law—I think we can do something. The lady, Miss Dunham, suffers great distress due to the trip across town. Yes, I think there is something here. . . ."

They sued. They won.

Could Katherine now have a room at the Grande Hotel?

"Take anything—take a whole floor!" the manager begged.

The tour went on, all over the world. At last Katherine's ambitions to travel were being realized. But in traveling on such a scale as this, it was hard, she found, to keep track of where she had been, where she was going next. Sometimes it was even difficult to know what town, what country, she was in, and what day it was. The days, the weeks, seemed to melt together. Many times, Katherine said to John, "I'm so glad I have you, and your good memory, along with me!"

Only incidents—funny, serious, sometimes frightening—stood out in Katherine's mind.

"What do they think we are?" Katherine asked her husband one day. "Are they afraid we are bringing something dangerous into the country?" She was very angry. This particular time the customs office, not content with merely examining their luggage, insisted on everything being spread out on the ground so that the customs men could take a closer look. That was bad enough. But there was snow on the ground!

"John, those costumes and sets will be ruined if we don't get them out of that slush!"

As always, John told her to be patient, that everything would work out. "You'll forget it by tomorrow—when something else will happen!"

The Dunham group usually consisted of 25 to 35 dancers and singers, and an orchestra. Katherine hired new members as she traveled and met people with talent. Many she trained herself. There might be drummers from Haiti and Cuba, and dancers from Brazil, Argentina, Mexico, Italy, and the United States. Eartha Kitt was a member for a time. So were Marlon Brando, James Dean, Chita Rivera, Betta St. John, Jennifer Jones, Bobby Capo.

Between tours, Katherine established the Katherine Dunham School of Cultural Arts, Inc., in New York City. It was "home base" for the group, and a wide range of courses was offered. The Dunham method of dance was taught, combining ballet with elements of Caribbean, African, and Central European dances. Each student was also offered classes in modern dance, tap dancing, Spanish, and Oriental dance, and classes in form and space, and form and function, in choreography, acting, anthropology, and languages.

The teachers were the most capable Katherine could find—Lee Strasberg, José Ferrer, Margaret Mead, Irene Hawthorne. With their talents, combined with Katherine's, it was no wonder so many students of the school went on to make names of their own in show business.

A writer who watched Katherine teach a class was delighted. She described the experience in an article for the magazine, *Dance and Dancers*.

She works to the beat of two drums and a pair of rattles, and a piano, seldom used, the writer explained.

The Cuban drummers sing in Spanish when the mood moves them, and there is a gay and care free feeling. Katherine dances in front of the group, which follows her from one end of the room to the other. She does different simple steps, hip and shoulder movements, to the beat of the drums. The group copies her movements. . . . Now and again in the middle of the moving, swaying mass, she corrects a wrong arm or a shoulder movement. Drums and the stamping of so many bare feet make you feel you are somewhere in Africa, watching a slender, long-legged village leader guiding her flock through the beat of a native dance. . . .

But Katherine was unable to spend as much time as she would have liked at the school. Her new show, *Bal Negre*, was so successful that its New York run was extended. Then Katherine took it on a tour across the country. She planned the dances for a musical show, *Windy City*. She and her company appeared at Carnegie Hall with a famous orchestra. She had already appeared as a guest artist with both the Los Angeles and the San Francisco orchestras.

Katherine and her dancers were the hit of the "pop" evening at Carnegie Hall. Then out to Hollywood again to appear in *Casbah*. Then it was time for Mexico City for a six-month engagement. Then a grand tour of Europe—London, Paris, Antwerp, Brussels, Liège, Nice, Monte Carlo, Italy, Switzerland.

Katherine's dances caused a sensation. One in particular was much discussed—the "Shango." Shango is the thunder god. A white cock must be sacrificed to him. The young boy chosen to kill the cock does so, then is possessed by Damballa, the snake god. The boy becomes a hissing, twisting snake. A priest controls him with spells, and the village is saved. For one moment, the possessed one stands, arms stretched out, on the altar, and is worshipped as a god. He faints, and is carried into the jungle. The dancing of the village people goes on. In the end, the boy is carried in triumph onto the stage on a sacred drum.

"Shango" actually combined elements from Trinidad, Haiti, and Cuba, but the words, music, and movements had come from Africa and had lasted in the New World for 300 years. An African who was visiting in London and went to see it, said it was very much like ceremonies still being performed in Nigeria.

A great hit in Europe was one which had amused American audiences for years—"Woman with a Cigar." Its setting was a Caribbean port on a hot afternoon. A boat docks, and a woman with a cigar brings baggage on shore. The natives, having nothing better to do, wonder about this creature. Where is she from? Mexico? Jamaica? Puerto Rico? Everyone enjoys the joke, which is the answer to the questions they have been asking one another. She is from Chicago! She is Katherine Dunham!

The Dunham group arrived in Paris a week before opening night—but their baggage did not. There was a serious transportation strike throughout France. Gun fire was even being exchanged between the two sides in the strike. Opening night came closer and closer, and still no baggage.

Katherine knew the baggage was somewhere between London and Paris. "After all, we had it when we left England, and it hasn't arrived here yet. It has to be *somewhere*. This strike!" she said bitterly.

"Wire your representatives in London. Have them search the channel ports," John suggested. "We have to get those trunks. All the costumes and sets are in them. The whole mood of the show will be lost unless we have them."

"Yes, this is one show you can't do in street clothes," Katherine agreed.

At last the baggage was found—one hundred pieces bearing the Dunham label—piled high in the streets of Cherbourg, serving as road blocks. For four days Katherine's agent pleaded with the police, with the striking workers, to release the trunks and suitcases and crates.

"No baggage can be moved. Haven't you heard? There's a strike on!" was the answer.

"Then opening night in Paris will come and go with no performance by Katherine Dunham and Company," her agent said. "Without these costumes and sets, she can't do the show."

"What's that you say? Katherine Dunham? The *artiste?*" asked the labor leader, in surprise.

"Exactly."

"The baggage—it is on its way to Paris," said the labor leader, and departed quickly to see that his promise was carried out. Perhaps he himself had a ticket for that opening night show!

The people of Paris adored Katherine Dunham, her dances, and her dancers. The engagement at the Palais de Chaillot was extended. The fans were so wild in showing their feeling that Katherine and John had to leave Paris and rent a house in the country, where they could find some peace and quiet between performances.

After her European tour, Katherine and her company made a return in triumph to Broadway.

In the Sunday New York *Times,* a reviewer wrote that whatever Katherine Dunham does in the theater, she does it with far more style and skill than she used to. She sings without raising her voice, dances with what seems like very little effort, makes those watching her understand her state of mind with the merest movement of a hip or ripple of a shoulder. She wears clothes or not with an easy sense of her personal beauty, which the Queen of Sheba might have envied. It is all cool, all smooth, all under control.

With all the constant traveling and success, Katherine's interest in books remained as strong as back in the days when she had been only reading of places instead of visiting them.

But now there was this difference—instead of only reading books, she was squeezing in time to write books herself. And they were being published and receiving the same praise that her dancing did. Her first book, *Journey to Accompong*, was hailed as a beautifully written account of her first year as an anthropologist.

Later, while spending a year in Japan, Katherine wrote a delightful story of her early life, called *A Touch of Innocence*. Those who reviewed it saw in it the same qualities which Katherine had been giving to the dance—honesty, humor, passion, and courage.

Back again in the United States. Katherine presented *Bambouche*, and it was generally agreed that she was better than ever.

The review pointed out that after an absence of seven years from Broadway, Katherine Dunham had returned with a cake walk, and even a belly dance, and the enthusiasm of a teen-ager. The man who wrote the review especially liked a dance called "Diamond Thief," set in South Africa. For another dance, "Marrakech," inspired by street dancers Katherine had seen in Morocco, she had brought dancers from Morocco itself, with special permission from King Hassan II.

Then came a commission from the great Metropolitan Opera Company. The opera assigned to Katherine was *Aïda*, about Egypt long ago. In it she was able to use a variety of styles, as one person pointed out: "Modern, belly dancing, the foot stamping and hip-and-shoulder shaking of native African dances, and much more."

A particularly interesting offer from Hollywood was a request to plan the dances for *Green Mansions*, a color film based on W. H. Hudson's novel. Mel Ferrer directed the production, and the cast included Audrey Hepburn, Anthony Perkins, Lee J. Cobb, and Sessue Hayakawa.

An article and photographs in *Dance* magazine showed Katherine Dunham kneeling over a tiny set, pointing out what she wanted of her dancers and drummers. She had done her own research in Brazil for the *Green Mansions* dances, which were trial and courage rites of the Marachusi tribes of South America's Brazilian jungles.

South American themes were always important in the Dunham dances.

"You know, I didn't give up anthropology, after all, back when I decided to put dance first," Katherine remarked thoughtfully.

"No," agreed John Pratt. "Wherever you travel as Katherine Dunham, dancer, you are also Katherine Dunham, anthropologist. You watch the dances done at ceremonies, and try to understand the meaning of those dances in the lives of the people."

"Yes, and a funny thing—I left university life and chose dancing instead of teaching for my profession, but I've been teaching all along. It has been rewarding. Very rewarding. Traveling to all the places I used to dream of seeing . . . discovering and training talented young people. Very rewarding indeed. All I dreamed about has come true—and much, much more."

CHAPTER 12

Back to Illinois

At last the telephone was silent. Katherine Dunham walked into the kitchen of the attractive apartment. She poured strong, black coffee into one of the blue-and-white cups she had brought back from her group's tour of Spain.

"John?" she called. "Do you want some coffee?" She knew he had just come upstairs to the apartment from the museum of her show business souvenirs housed on the floor below. He'd been taking care of most of the phone calls. He probably needed a moment of rest more than she did.

Taking down another cup, she filled it, then carried both to the living room. Before she sat down, she pulled the drapes over the windows to hide the gray winter scene outside.

So different, she thought as she sat down, from the many homes she and John had had in warm countries. And better, much better, she reminded herself, than the Chicago slums where she had once lived. A smile touched her eyes. Who would ever have expected that skinny little brown girl from Chicago's South Side slums to become a famous dancer? To be in Hollywood movies and have her own Broadway shows? And now, to be Artist in Residence here at Southern Illinois University?

With her dancer's grace, Katherine sank down on the black sofa. On the low coffee table in front of her was a gold key—the Key to the City that the mayor had given her when she had come here to the university.

"Come on, John," she called. "Please come here and help me remember."

But it was company she really wanted. Remembering wasn't hard. It would be harder not to remember all the years, all the places. There were so many things surrounding her here, souvenirs from all over the world. Even Katherine's clothes—thin sandals from Rome, slacks and shirt from New York, the scarf on her head from Africa, tied the African way.

And downstairs, all the scrap books of the newspaper stories and photographs of her on stage. The drum room, with the big African drum-harp hanging in the air (and pulling the light, to which it was attached, slightly crooked). In the hall, there were old posters for slave sales or offering rewards for slaves who had run away.

And there were the young student dancers, as full of ambition and as much in love with life as she had been during her own college days. She hoped they would be as successful as some of her previous students . . . that dancing would give them lives as interesting as her own had been!

John Pratt wandered in and looked down at her with a twinkle in his blue eyes. "Now, what's all this about helping you remember?" he wanted to know, teasing her. "Considering your mother says you used to claim you could remember when you were born, and how the horse was frightened by a butterfly on the trip home from the hospital . . . !"

Katherine grinned at him. "Well, then, just keep me company while I remember. The head of a publishing company wants a book written about my life, and sent a long list of questions about my career, and asked if I could give them any stories."

John's eyes twinkled again, and his silver mustache

curved upward as he laughed. "Can you give them any! The question would be, *which* to give them!"

"Yes, and the very best ones are always the ones we can't share," Katherine agreed. "The ones which involve people who'd rather write their own stories than be in one about me."

John came over and lowered his six-foot-plus frame to sit beside Katherine on the sofa. He looked at the pile of papers, the questions from the New York publishing company. "Hmm—they want to know if you are a writing a new book now."

"*Island Possessed*—at least, I hope that's what it will still be called, by the time it's published," Katherine said, nodding. "About Haiti, as seen through the eyes of a research student."

John was still studying the list of questions. "These shouldn't be too difficult, not with your memory. They want a lot of dates, don't they? May take some checking, but I can track them down, even if it means opening up the boxes." There were still boxes and boxes of Katherine's souvenirs which they hadn't even begun to put away.

Katherine's eyes were looking over the list of questions. Oh, what memories they did stir up! "John, look at this. Do you remember . . . ?"

Katherine Dunham had come full circle—back to her

native Illinois, to her mother's home town of Alton, in fact. Just across the river was St. Louis and Chouteau Street, where a long-ago ceremony had sparked her interest in customs and dances.

Now she had degrees after her name. She had been honored in her own country and abroad. She had been elected to membership and high office in such professional organizations as the American Guild of Musical Artists, the American Guild of Variety Artists, the American Federation of Radio Artists, Actors' Equity, and the Negro Actors' Guild.

It had been said that Katherine Dunham is to dance what Marian Anderson is to song. That means a great deal. What also means a great deal is that she has earned a place in world culture as Pioneer of the Negro Dance.

"There's one draw back that I can see," John remarked, glancing up from the pages of questions. At Katherine's look, he said, "You've done more in your life than any ten ordinary—or not-so-ordinary—other people have in theirs. But your life's by no means near its end yet. I'm just wondering what more you'll accomplish during the rest of it."